Michael Wa

Charles Richard Drew

Charles Richard Drew

Pioneer in Blood Research

By Richard Hardwick

Charles Scribner's Sons New York

For Peggy, Amy, Caroline, and Lynn

A–9.67[V]

Printed in the United States of America
Library of Congress Catalog Card Number 67-24049

Contents

1	A Boy with Curiosity	7
2	Foggy Bottom	11
3	A Star on the Rise	24
4	"The Best Player I Ever Coached"	33
5	A New Day at Morgan College	47
6	Medical School in Canada	61
7	The Lamp of Learning	74
8	At the Frontiers of Science	87
9	Striving Upward: *Banked Blood*	99
10	Time of Crisis	111
11	Blood for Britain	122
12	Howard University: New Worlds	133
	Glossary	141
	Sources	142
	Index	143

Grateful acknowledgment is made for permission to quote from the following: "The Best Player I Ever Coached" by D. O. McLaughry, *The Saturday Evening Post*. Copyright © 1952, The Curtis Publishing Company; Emma Gelders Sterne, THE BLOOD BROTHERS: Four Men of Science (New York, Alfred A. Knopf, 1959.) Copyright © 1959 by Emma Gelders Sterne.

1 A Boy with Curiosity

It was a hot night in the summer of 1912. The boards of a wooden stage on the grounds of the old Octagon House rattled beneath the tapping and shuffling feet of Bert Williams and his troupe of minstrels. Across Seventeenth Street, the strains of music carried through the open windows of the White House.

From the rows of wooden benches arrayed before the stage, upturned faces laughed, hands applauded enthusiastically, and voices joined in the familiar choruses of the songs. Unnoticed by either performers or audience was a small figure crawling carefully along the low limb of an oak tree that extended over the stage.

"You better come back off of there!" came a concerned whisper from the fork of the tree.

The boy paused only long enough to turn his head and glance back in the darkness toward his friend. "I just want to get a better look, Eddie. I'll be right over them if I can get out a little farther."

"Sure!" came the whispered reply. "*If* you get out there! But supposing you fall off? You better come back here!"

A determined grin crept over the youthful face. "Stop worrying so much. I'm not going to fall!" He looked down at the performers. Bert Williams stood at the front of the stage just behind the gas footlights, his arms spread wide, his voice lifted in a popular song as a dozen banjoes strummed out the rhythm.

The boy inched his way along the limb, and a little shower of bark powdered down onto the stage. One of the banjo players paused to brush at his nose, thinking perhaps it was merely an insect attracted by the lights.

Suddenly, sure-footed though he was, the boy's legs slipped. He grabbed desperately with both arms while trying frantically to pull a leg up and hook it over the limb. At the same time, he wished belatedly that he had been paying more attention to what he was doing, rather than being so absorbed in what was going on below.

People who had been intent on the show now looked up to behold the strange apparition dangling from amid the dark leaves, wondering perhaps if this might be a part of the act.

Short brown legs kicked and swung valiantly in their effort to regain the relative obscurity of the tree as, one by one, the performers on stage looked up. The music faded and stopped. The great Bert Williams himself turned to see what was causing the disturbance.

The boy, suddenly aware that he was the sole center of attention, lost his grip entirely and came plummeting down. His bare feet struck the boards at a point approximately midway between Mr. Bones and Mr. Interlocutor. He tumbled, and as quickly as he had taken his fall, came bounding agilely to his feet with a startled expression on his face.

From beyond the footlights there was a roar of laughter.

"Well, now," Bert Williams drawled, hands on hips and his head cocked to one side, "I've heard tell o' folks that'd do pretty near anything to get into vaudeville, but ain't this goin' just a bit too far, sonny boy?"

The laughter of the crowd swelled, but from offstage to the right, a man who was definitely not smiling came striding out. This was trouble, and the boy's eyes darted about for the best avenue of escape.

"Grab him!" the man boomed. "Grab that kid!"

But the boy had already taken to his heels, fleet as a rabbit. He made his exit, stage left, as fast as his sturdy legs could pump, hit the ground, and without breaking stride scampered away into the protective darkness. By the time he stopped running, the sounds of the minstrel show were far behind. The banjoes were strumming again, the voices of the minstrel troupe soft on the Washington summer air. The youngster caught his breath and strolled back toward the show. As he drew near the crowd, his friend Eddie fell into step beside him.

"Weren't you scared?" Eddie asked with undisguised admiration. "I mean, being right up there on the stage and that manager chasing you the way he did? Boy! Was he mad! And he pretty near caught you, too."

The boy glanced around at his friend. He could easily shrug the incident off, now that it was over, and say it hadn't scared him at all. "Sure, I was scared," he admitted. "Who wouldn't have been? But I got a good look, and Bert Williams himself said something to me."

"Suppose they had grabbed you?"

"They didn't," he said. But even as he walked along, his thoughts were moving ahead to practical matters. Mama and Papa were out there in the audience, and they had surely seen who it was that fell out of the tree in the middle of the show. They had probably laughed along with everybody else, but he had a feeling they wouldn't think it was so funny by the time they got home. He rubbed his backside apprehensively.

Charles Richard Drew, eight years old, had just made his first public appearance quite by accident.

2 Foggy Bottom

In the late 1800's and early 1900's, in Washington, D.C., along the Potomac River to the south and southeast of Georgetown, there was an area known as Foggy Bottom. The name was the logical result of the dense mists that drifted across the low, marshy ground from the Potomac. Because of the dampness, it was not the healthiest place in the city, and because it was not desirable real estate, it was a place relegated to those on the lower rungs of the economic ladder, both white and Negro.

It was here in Foggy Bottom, on June 3, 1904, that Charles Drew was born. The young mother and father,

Nora and Richard Drew, lived with Richard's parents in an old house on Twenty-first Street. The fog from the river that night was unusually heavy, swirling slowly along the unpaved street, forming glowing haloes about the occasional street lights, and muting the sounds of horses and wagons.

The midwife had arrived, and Richard Drew waited anxiously at the foot of the stairs, glancing frequently at the closed door on the landing.

A friend clapped him on the back. "Take it easy. You'll worry yourself to death. Everything's going to be all right."

"It's been a long time. I wonder if anything's wrong——"

At that moment there was a lusty cry from above, and minutes later the midwife opened the door and stepped to the banister, smiling down at the tall young man. "It's a boy, Mr. Drew. Nora and the baby are both just fine. You can come up in a little while and see them."

Richard Drew sighed deeply. Suddenly, he began to search his pockets, then he smiled around at his father and the friends who had kept the vigil with him. "I'm afraid I forgot all about getting any cigars," he said.

Richard Drew was a carpet layer by trade. It was hard work, with a considerable degree of skill required. His pay was sufficient to keep his family in modest circumstances, but as that family grew—first little Charlie, then Elsa, Joe, Nora, and years later,

Eva—it became even more necessary to watch every penny spent. The fact was, no matter how skilled he became, how much promise he showed, or how hard he worked, the positions and opportunities above carpet layer were closed to a Negro. He had already reached the limit of his ability to produce income. The Emancipation Proclamation freeing the slaves had become law more than forty years before. The Civil War had been over nearly as long, yet the Negro, in the South and in the North, found himself virtually stymied at the bottom of the social and economic ladder. Drew was, perhaps, more fortunate than most, but this did not prevent his seeing that the only way to break out was through education, and this he vowed to give to his children.

A few years after Charles was born, and after the arrival of his brother Joe and sister Elsa, the young family moved a few blocks away to E Street into the big, rambling house where Nora's parents, the Burrels, lived. It was still Foggy Bottom, still little more than a slum. The houses were old and always in need of repair. The unpaved streets became rivers of mud after a rain and stayed that way long after the sun came out because of the poor drainage of the low-lying land.

But the house was bigger, and there were sections of vacant land where the children could play without having to go into the streets. There was also Grandpa Joe Burrel, who worked as a dog catcher for the city of Washington. Grandpa Joe, in the course of his work, had acquired a small pack of fighting terriers. He was also a fancier of fighting cocks, all of which he kept in well-tended pens in the yard behind the house. All week—Monday through Saturday—he drove his horse-drawn wagon up and down the streets and avenues of the capital, scooping up stray dogs and carting them off to the pound. On Sunday, though, while the rest of the family went to church, Grandpa Joe and some of his friends would load the cocks and dogs into their wagons and drive into Maryland or across the Potomac into Virginia to the fighting pits.

This was a source of wonder to the two boys, Charlie and Joe, and they often begged him to allow them to go along.

The old man would shake his head. "It's not for boys. You go on to church with your folks; that's where you ought to be."

Richard and Nora took the children down to the Nineteenth Street Baptist Church to attend Sunday school and listen to the fiery sermons of Reverend Brooks. They sang in the choir, and they gave what they could to the church. Weather permitting, when church was over, Nora Drew made a picnic lunch and the whole family spent the afternoon on the Monument Grounds or on the White House lawn to hear a band concert.

It was usually late on Sunday evening when Grandpa Joe and his friends returned. Sometimes the mood was one of jubilation, the men singing and laughing and recounting tales of the fights to which the young boys would listen with rapt attention. These were the times when Grandpa brought home more money than he took with him.

Other times the men returned in silence, with only the creak of the wagon harnesses and perhaps the whimpering of the injured dogs. Often there were broken, bloody bodies of cocks and dogs that had gone out so scrappily in the morning and the solemn occasion of burying the fallen gladiators. Later the men would go home to get what sleep they could before the workday that lay ahead.

The fights were illegal, but the practice was widespread. It was an exciting, if cruel, sport, with the added lure of a man being able to bet on the animals he had trained. The events were attended by white and Negro alike, both drawn by the same attraction.

But it was, as Grandpa Joe had said, "Not for boys," and Charlie and Joe were never allowed more than stories of what went on. There were other things they could do, however. In the summer, when the boys were young, Richard Drew took them to the Potomac River at the foot of G Street. There, diving from the sand and gravel barges that tied up along the Washington waterfront, he taught the boys to swim. They took to the water like fish, and in almost no time they were as expert as their father. Because there were no swimming pools in Washington open to Negroes when Charlie Drew was a small boy, he spent most of the days of summer splashing around in the Potomac, as did hundreds of other children from Foggy Bottom.

In 1912, the Young Men's Christian Association

opened a branch on Twelfth Street, and here, for the first time, a gymnasium and swimming pool were made available to Negro youths. The same year a smaller pool for Negroes opened on the Monument Grounds, and while these were strictly segregated facilities, it was a step up from the river.

The following year a third pool was opened at the playground near the Mott School, which was closer to the Drews' home. Charlie was there from opening till closing time, every day he could manage. It was not long before the head lifeguard took notice of the boy's exceptional swimming ability, and one day he called him aside.

"You're pretty good, son. What's your name?"

The youngster pulled himself up and wiped the water from his face. "Charlie Drew."

"How old are you, Charlie?"

"I'm eight years old."

The lifeguard looked the boy up and down. "You're big for your age. I'd have guessed you were closer to ten."

Charlie smiled. "No, sir. Just eight this month."

"You look like a pretty fair swimmer. We're going to have a swimming meet here on the Fourth of July. You thought about entering it?"

Charlie's eyes widened with surprise. "I didn't know I was old enough."

"There's a division for the younger boys. Well, how about it?"

The bronze, freckled face broke into a grin. "Sure! What time do we start!"

The lifeguard laughed. "Hold on! It's still a week off. You'd better keep practicing, though, and on the Fourth bring along a lunch."

Charlie needed no more encouragement. The thought of competing in a real swimming meet excited him. He had raced with Joe and the other boys plenty of times down on the river, as well as swum impromptu races in the pools, but never before in an official contest. Perhaps it was some trait inherited from Grandpa Joe Burrel that drove Charlie in this direction, but the time between that day and July 4 could not pass quickly enough to suit him.

The Fourth arrived at last, bright and hot. Bands played and marched up Pennsylvania Avenue. President Taft paused long enough in his campaigning against Teddy Roosevelt to make a speech on the White House lawn. There was a great feeling in the air, an electric excitement.

But for Charlie Drew, there was something more. It was a feeling that was natural with him—the anticipation of competition, of matching his own skills and abilities against those of others.

Charlie, Joe, and a dozen other boys headed for the Mott playground, pausing along the way to watch a parade or listen to a band. The pool was noisy and crowded as the meet got under way. First, there were diving competitions and the races for the older age groups. Charlie watched them all, anxiously awaiting his turn. Finally, the time came. Charlie and the other eight-year-olds lined up at the end of the pool. The head lifeguard stood to the side, waiting until all the contestants were in place.

"All right, boys! On your mark! Get set! *Go!*"

Charlie lunged out in the flat racing dive he had been practicing and felt the cool rush of the water as he began his smooth stroke. He reached the far end of the pool, made an expert turn, and struck out in the opposite direction. As he turned his head for a breath, he saw that many of the others were still struggling along on the first lap. By the time Charlie reached the second turn, he was far ahead of his nearest competitor. Above the sounds of the water, he heard someone—it sounded like Joe—yell, "Come on, Charlie! You got 'em! Come on!"

He ended the final lap, touched the rough concrete, and pulled himself up from the water. As he rubbed his hands across his face and gasped down deep, satisfying breaths of air, he saw that the boy coming in second had only begun the final lap.

A tired but happy Charlie Drew, just turned eight years old, took home four medals that night and placed them proudly on the mantel in the big living room of the house in Foggy Bottom.

But growing up in Foggy Bottom was not all going to church and having picnics and winning swimming meets. Foggy Bottom was, at best, a rough neighborhood—at worst, a ghetto. It was a place where people had to stand up for themselves. This applied to adults as well as children. There was an informal education to be had on the streets, and Charlie Drew, like all the others, would be influenced by it.

One summer Grandpa Joe gave him a ball for his birthday, and on a morning soon afterward, Charlie walked down the dusty street toward the river, bouncing it against a broken-down wooden fence along the way. The ball struck the planking and came bounding back toward him. But as Charlie reached up to take it, another hand seemed to pop out of nowhere and snag the ball.

"Got it!" the boy cried. Charlie knew him. He lived in the next block, and he was two years older than Charlie and a head taller. He was also known around the neighborhood as a bully.

"Hey! That's my ball!" Charlie yelled, grabbing for it.

The boy twisted away, and laughing over his shoulder, went running off down the street. It was goodbye ball, Charlie told himself, unless he went after it. So he sprinted off in hot pursuit, his legs pumping furiously. He was very fast on his feet, and within a block he caught up to the larger boy and brought him to the ground with a flying tackle.

"Give me back that ball!"

The ball popped from the boy's hands and

bounced into a flower bed in front of a small frame house. The encounter had gone beyond the question of who got the ball. Charlie had made his challenge, and other boys seemed to come from all directions at the smell of a battle.

"Fight!" they yelled gleefully. *"Fight!"*

"Give it to him!"

"Let him have one in the breadbasket, Charlie!"

"Come on, Charlie, don't let him shove you around!"

Charlie stood his ground, still ready to call it quits without a fight. Both boys were on their feet now, nose to nose. "All I want is my ball," Charlie said, looking the other boy straight in the eye.

His answer was a roundhouse right that caught him against the side of the head. Forcing back the tears, he put his head down and charged in, punching and kicking for all he was worth. Down they went, rolling and tumbling about in the street, stirring a cloud of dust as the crowd yelled and cheered them on.

A horse and wagon rumbled by, turned the corner, and then the ring about the combatants suddenly parted. The yelling died down as a large woman broke through, her voluminous skirts swirling about her as she snatched each of the boys up by one arm and held them apart. She showed no surprise upon recognizing the older boy. She had seen him fighting in the streets before. But when she turned and her gaze fell on Charlie, her eyes widened.

"Well! Charles Drew! What on earth are you doing

out here brawling in the streets! Your Mama's going to give you a tanning you won't soon forget!"

"Let 'em fight, Miz Smith," muttered some of the disappointed onlookers.

"All you boys scat! *Get!*"

Charlie glanced at his opponent, who was busy wiping a bloody nose on a ripped and dirty sleeve. He lowered his eyes to his own clothes, which were torn just as badly, and he knew that Mrs. Smith was right. He was in for a tanning. He lifted his free hand to his mouth. His two front teeth were considerably looser than they had been a few minutes before.

"We . . . we were just playing, ma'am," he offered tentatively.

"Playing, my *foot!* Next time you want to play that way, you keep away from around my flower bed!" She gave them a last withering glance and marched back into the little house.

The boys stood facing each other silently for several moments. Then the older boy walked over to the flower bed and picked up the ball. He tossed it into the air once, and Charlie braced himself to resume the battle. But with a laugh, the boy flipped the ball to him. "You fight pretty good, Charlie." Then, seriously, he added, "I mean, for a kid your age."

Charlie rolled the ball between his hands and grinned back. "Want to play some catch and walk down to the river?"

The other boy's smile broadened, and he wiped again unconsciously at his nose. "Sure. Why not?"

Fighting was not all that young Charlie Drew was learning in the streets of Foggy Bottom, though it might have seemed that way. He was learning a far more important lesson—self-reliance and how to get along with those around him under any circumstances. But if it came to a fight, then fight he would.

Charlie began his formal education at Briggs Elementary School. He was a good student from the beginning—bright, inquisitive, with an exceptional ability to grasp new ideas and concepts. His enthusiasm for athletics continued to grow through the years that followed, spreading into every sport that was open to him. When, as a fifth grader, he transferred to Stevens Elementary School, Charlie was already showing great promise as a budding football player.

Like many boys, he took on a newspaper route. But unlike most boys, Charlie Drew made a thorough analysis of its potential and came up with a plan.

He began with the *Washington Star*, and enlisting the aid of his brother Joe (at a fair percentage of the profit), sold the papers outside government buildings as the workers left for the day. It was the practice of various governmental departments to stagger the hours at which the shifts ended, and Charlie immediately saw he was losing sales by not being able to get to all the buildings in his area in time to catch the departing employees.

"I've got an idea," he told Joe one afternoon. "We'll need five or six more boys to do it, and we'll need a schedule of all the departments so we'll know when to have the papers there."

The two rounded up half a dozen friends, and Charlie mapped out the schedule, assigning each boy to a certain government building at a certain time. The plan went like clockwork, and before long he had added the *Herald* and the *Post* to his inventory. The young entrepreneur's force of employees reached a total of twelve boys, with sales of some two thousand papers a day. At a gross profit of a penny a copy, Charlie met his overhead and managed to net almost five dollars a day for himself.

Idle time was something he never thought of, and even with the profitable newspaper sales organization, he continued to participate in all athletic activities offered at school, as well as keeping up creditably with his academic work.

As the end of his last year in elementary school drew near, Charlie turned the newspaper business over to Joe and found a somewhat less demanding job working afternoons as a special-delivery boy for the Post Office. He was looking forward impatiently to the high school years that lay ahead. There were football, baseball, basketball, and track, and he had already made up his mind he was going out for every one of them.

3 A Star on the Rise

"Set your sights high," Nora Drew told her children. "Just remember, you have to work to get there. And education is at the bottom of it all."

Nora and Richard Drew had agreed long before their first child was born that they would do everything in their power to assure each child as much education as possible. Nora Drew was a graduate of Washington's Miner Normal, a teachers' school, and before marrying had planned to become a teacher. Richard Drew, on the other hand, had found it impossible to continue his education after completing high school, and he felt that he might well have advanced further in other directions if he had been able to go to college.

Young Charlie Drew had the great advantage of parents with foresight. And the fact that he was born and raised in Washington proved, in at least one way, to have been very fortunate. It meant that when the time came he could enter Paul Laurence Dunbar High School, which had long been recognized as perhaps the finest Negro high school in the entire country. Originally known simply as the M Street School, it had been renamed to honor a young Negro poet, Paul Dunbar, who died in 1906.

It was a proud school, with an unusually high percentage of its graduates going on to college, many of them on scholarships. Dunbar High counts among its alumni a large number of the top Negro scholars and professional men in the United States. They include Benjamin O. Davis, who became the first Negro general in the United States Army; federal judge and former governor of the Virgin Islands, William Hastie; brain surgeon, Dr. Clarence Green; psychologist, W. Allison Davis; baritone, Lawrence Winters; and many others.

Charlie Drew entered Dunbar in 1918, just as the devastating First World War was coming to a close. The academic record Charlie made during the four years that followed was not particularly outstanding, though it was obvious to his teachers that he had a quick mind and would undoubtedly have done better had all his energies been directed toward scholastic achievement.

His keenest interest was in athletics, and in that area he set records that still stand. He went out for every sport offered. In the fall he was running and throwing on the football field. In winter he made a name for himself on the basketball court. In the spring there was the crack of the bat in baseball and sprinting and jumping on the cinder track.

Charlie Drew excelled in them all, becoming a four-letter man well before his senior year. His interests did not begin and end with sports. He was popular among his classmates, boys and girls alike, and became captain of Company E, Third Regiment, of the Cadet Corps. In both his junior and senior years, under the expert eye of Coach Edwin Henderson, Charlie won the James E. Walker Memorial medal as best all-round athlete. No student had ever before won the medal two years, and after Charlie Drew's feat, it was ruled that future athletes would be eligible to receive it for one year only.

But if Charlie was a hero at school, he was something less than that when he brought a report card home to show his parents. His grades were passing, with many of them above average, but for Nora Drew this was not enough.

"It's not as if you couldn't do better, son," she chastened him. Then, looking at the huge letter D on his jacket, she said, "Football and baseball aren't everything." She was a tiny woman, but what she lacked in size she more than made up in determination and authority. Her children idolized her, and when Mama Drew spoke, they listened.

Charlie nodded glumly. "I know, Mama. I'll work harder next semester."

His father saw the potential athletic greatness in his son, but he saw too that athletic prowess in a Negro held far less promise for the future than did scholastic prowess. No matter how good a football or baseball player a Negro youth was, there was no place for him in the professional field. It would be many years before a young Negro named Jackie Robinson would break through the color barrier.

Charlie did not lessen his efforts in athletics. He simply intensified his studying, and his grades began to come up accordingly. He also kept his part-time job and continued to put money aside toward his college education.

The Drew family had been more fortunate than many in the early years of the century. Richard Drew became the only Negro member of the carpet layers union of the American Federation of Labor and consequently was able to make a better salary than he might have otherwise. The children were bright and healthy, and the future seemed secure.

But in 1918, as the war ended, a terrible epidemic of influenza swept over the whole world. People died by the millions—more than twelve million in India alone and a half million in the United States, despite its far superior medical facilities. The nation's capital was particularly hard hit, and tragedy struck thousands of families, among them the Drews. Elsa came home from school one afternoon complaining of a stomachache. Nora Drew put the child to bed. By nightfall her condition had worsened, chills and fever set in, and her entire body ached. She tried not to cry, but as the illness became worse, the child could not hold back the tears.

A doctor was called, but with the disease sweeping the entire city, it was almost impossible to get one to come. Finally, at nearly midnight, the tired physician arrived. It was almost a foregone conclusion, and after an examination of the young girl, he stepped out into the hallway with Nora and Richard Drew.

"It's the flu, just as I suspected," he told them. "Keep her in bed, and keep the other children out of the room." He took a small vial from his bag. "Give her a teaspoon of this every two hours. I'll stop in tomorrow and have a look."

"Is—is it a bad case?" the anxious father asked.

The doctor sighed. "They're all bad." He put on his coat, picked up his bag. "Perhaps the day will come when we'll be better able to cope with this."

Young Charlie had heard what the doctor had said and had seen the weary frustration on the man's face. In his studies at Dunbar, Charlie had read of some of the great men of medicine—Pasteur, Harvey, Jenner. There had been great strides taken over the centuries, but there was still a great deal that doctors were powerless against.

The days passed slowly. Hearses were a common

sight on the streets of the city as the epidemic took its toll. School classes were canceled, and most people were fearful of venturing out of their homes. Each day Elsa seemed to grow weaker. The doctor, tired and haggard, and continually exposed to the disease himself, did everything he could. But it was not enough, and less than a week after contracting the disease, the child died.

It was a time of grief for the entire family, but for Charlie, it was something more. At fourteen, helplessly watching his sister die despite all the doctor could do and seeing the constant, slow procession of hearses moving through the city, he first began to think of medicine as his possible life's work.

The epidemic ended at last. The schools were reopened, and life went on. Charlie Drew, while his scholastic record continued to show improvement, was becoming an outstanding athlete. Competition for the teams was unusually stiff in the years following the war. There was no age limit for students, and it was not uncommon to have high school classmates as old as twenty-five, who were usually young men returning from the armed services to continue their education.

Charlie had always been large for his age, however. By the time he was sixteen, he was almost six feet tall, and weighed over 175 pounds. When school was out for the summer, he would take a job on a road gang or heavy construction project—any type of work that would help keep him in physical trim.

Toward the end of his junior year at Dunbar, a friend, Lincoln Johnson, caught up with Charlie after classes one day.

"Have you heard about the jobs Mr. Westmoreland has got set up for the summer?"

Charlie shook his head. "What are they?"

"Working in a glass factory up in New Jersey. Think you'll sign up?"

Edgar Westmoreland was the vocational director at Dunbar High, and every summer he tried to place all students who wanted work in temporary jobs. Charlie thought about it for a moment. He had been considering work on a road construction job in Virginia, but he had never been farther from Washington than Virginia and Maryland.

"Maybe I'll do that," he said. "I'll see Mr. Westmoreland about it first thing tomorrow."

The pay was good, and Westmoreland assured Charlie that the work would be hard, so when the train pulled out for Salem, New Jersey, early in June, Charlie Drew was one of several dozen Dunbar boys aboard. In Salem they were housed in a dormitory near the glass works. From the first day, the work proved to be almost back-breaking, shoveling and hauling sand, working close to the furnaces where the temperature stayed well over the 100 degree mark. At day's end, the boys were dirty, sweaty, and bone-tired. It wasn't long before each train heading toward Washington had a few of the boys aboard.

One night in the dormitory a weary Lincoln Johnson dropped down on his cot. He looked across at Charlie and could not suppress a laugh. Charlie had got too close to one of the huge furnaces and had singed away his eyebrows and was virtually bald halfway back on top of his head.

"You ought to see yourself, Charlie!"

"I already did. Maybe it'll grow back before summer's over."

Linc clasped his hands behind his head and became serious. "It's been three weeks now, and there're less than half of us still here." He glanced again at his friend. "Are you going to stick it out?"

"Sure. Why not?"

Linc sighed. "I sort of figured you would. There're six of us taking the train home tomorrow, Charlie. I wish you'd go with us. We can find some kind of work in Washington."

Charlie grimaced and rubbed at his almost hairless face. "Looking like this? No, I'll wait awhile."

The talk about his eyebrows growing back was only his way of letting his friend know he was going to stay. The determination to stick with whatever he started was one of the traits that was to remain with Charles Drew throughout his life. It was not mere blind stubbornness that made him do it. It was the ultimate goal. In this case it was the money he was making, which he would apply toward his college fund. The work was hard, but he didn't mind that.

When the summer was over and it was time to get back to school, there was only one Washington boy still working at the glass factory in Salem, New Jersey. It was Charlie Drew.

Charlie was a campus hero throughout his four years at Dunbar High. His status as an outstanding athlete was perhaps the prime reason for this, but he also had the sort of personality that naturally drew people to him. In his senior year he was voted most popular boy, best athlete, the student that did the most for Dunbar High during his four years, and in the yearbook, beneath his picture, his classmates wrote facetiously:

"Charlie Drew, vice-president of the Chicago-Milwaukee Electric Railroad, attended the reception with his pretty Boston wife."

It might easily have come true if Charlie had set his sights on a railroading career and on Boston as the place to look for a wife.

4 "The Best Player I Ever Coached"

Charles Richard Drew graduated from Dunbar High in 1922, with a scholarship to Amherst College, in Massachusetts. He had not yet determined what his goal in life would be. Having worked several summers with construction crews, he leaned somewhat toward engineering. But the memory of the terrible influenza epidemic and little Elsa's death was still fresh, and a possible medical career was in the back of his mind.

A good friend from Washington, Montague Cobb, had gone on to Amherst the year before. Cobb was also a Dunbar graduate, as was William Hastie, who began his college work at Amherst along with Charlie. Even though segregation was not a practice at Amherst as it was in southern schools, the Negro students were a small minority of the student body and as such tended to gravitate toward each other. Charlie's roommate in South Hall was George Gilmer, another Negro youth from Washington.

Charlie began the regular freshman curriculum, but just as at Dunbar, he set his sights high in athletics. His reputation had preceded him and had been a factor in his receiving a scholarship. On the first day of football tryouts, Charlie, Monty Cobb, and George Gilmer were on the field, suited up and ready. The head coach at Amherst was D.O. McLaughry, known more familiarly as "Tuss" McLaughry.

The coach immediately sensed that extra something in the tall, well-built Negro freshman from Washington. In practice he showed a lightning-like getaway, and he possessed the second effort that can mean the crucial extra yard or two. As a passer, even with the old pumpkin-shaped football, Charlie had deadly accuracy. The mid-twenties were long before the days of offensive and defensive platoons, and Charlie could tackle and break up a pass play with the best of them.

Charlie Drew was immediately in his element at Amherst. Even though he waited on tables at various places around the college town to supplement his scholarship, he found time for his studies and his athletic endeavors. He made a good showing in all four major sports his freshman year, and that summer returned to Washington to take a job as lifeguard at the Francis Swimming Pool.

The following fall, Charlie was well on his way to football stardom. There were three Negro players on the team—Charlie, Monty Cobb, and George Gilmer. Toward the end of the season came the big game, the one with arch-rival Wesleyan University. The stands were jammed to capacity. The cold December wind, carrying flurries of snow, swept across the field in sporadic gusts, making passing uncertain at best. At the end of the field the scoreboard clock swept relentlessly toward the last seconds of the game with the Amherst Lord Jeffs trailing the Wesleyan Cardinals by 6 to 10. Some of the fans were already beginning to move toward the exits.

Charlie Drew, playing quarterback, spoke to his disheartened squad in what was obviously going to be the last huddle before the gun. The Wesleyan goal line was an impossible forty yards away, with a determined Cardinal squad guarding it.

Charlie glanced momentarily downfield, then bent over. "We'll try a pass. Gilmer, you and McBride get downfield. Whoever gets clear, I'll throw it to him."

"It's going to be tough with this wind, Charlie," said one of the tackles.

Charlie Drew grinned. "You just keep those boys away from me as long as you can. I'll handle the pass. It's the only chance we've got."

The purple-and-white-clad team jogged into position. Charlie stood several yards behind the center as the two teams lined up. The crowd in the stands grew quiet, and those nearing the exits paused to watch the final play.

Charlie barked the signal: "Twenty-one, thirty-two, eighteen, *hike!*"

The ball spiraled back, and leather met leather as the forward wall of Wesleyan battered toward the man with the ball.

Charlie dropped back, his keen eyes darting from Gilmer to McBride, both of whom were streaking downfield toward the goal. But neither man was in the clear, and Charlie deftly sidestepped a would-be tackler. Another got a hand briefly on his passing arm, and Drew twisted away to his right. Gilmer was guarded, but far down the field McBride had outdistanced his man. The tacklers swarmed in now past the defense. A Wesleyan player had Charlie by the right leg, another grappled him around the waist, and a third piled in. Literally pulling the tacklers with him, Drew cocked his arm, made a powerful, smooth motion, and the pigskin was on its way.

The crowd in the stands was on its feet, every eye on the spiraling ball. McBride was almost at the Wesleyan goal line, completely in the clear. The ball arced over the field, and without missing a stride, McBride reached up and pulled it in.

Far back upfield, Charlie Drew had disappeared beneath a wave of red and black uniforms, but the roar of the crowd told him what he wanted to know. He had hit his man. Amherst had pulled it out of the fire.

The Wesleyan game was the beginning of a new team at Amherst. Morale soared, and the boys felt unbeatable with Charlie Drew calling the plays. As Coach Tuss McLaughry was to write many years later: "The victory with Wesleyan in 1923 built such team faith in Drew [that] he was able to lead Amherst to its largest scores in Little Three (Amherst, Wesleyan, and Williams) history at its peak two seasons later in 1925. That year Amherst lost only to Princeton and, even in losing, Drew gained more than 160 yards and was the outstanding man on the field."

The winning streak continued on through 1926, which was the year after both Drew and Coach Tuss McLaughry left the college.

As he went into his junior year at Amherst, Charlie Drew was still leaning more toward engineering than medicine as a career. His grades ranged from D's to A's, but he kept his average above C, principally because the scholarship was based on his scholastic average. He received three-fourths of his tuition if he maintained a C or better, and so he managed to keep it high enough.

While his principal interest was in athletics, it was significant that his highest grades were in biology and related subjects, in which he made straight A's. Dr. Otto Glaser was professor of biology at the time, and Charlie spent many hours in the laboratories under his guidance. Glaser saw a unique ability in the bright young man as he meticulously dissected a frog or worked over a term paper on such subjects as fluid distribution in the embryo. Much of what Charles Drew learned under Dr. Glaser was to play an important part years later.

An accident was also to play a key role in deciding Charlie's future. During a football game against Williams in 1925, he received a bad leg injury and was hospitalized. The injury, on the inside of his thigh, became badly infected, and Charlie spent several weeks in the hospital. Unaccustomed to being restricted in physical acitvity, he occupied himself in keeping up with his studies and observing the doctors and nurses at their work.

One afternoon, as his doctor was changing the dressing on the leg, Charlie struck up a conversation.

"How's it look, doctor?" he said.

"It's getting better. I think we'll be turning you loose in a few days now."

"I'm going to miss the place."

The doctor looked at him curiously. "Miss the hospital? The star of the Amherst team? A fellow who's used to being on the move all the time? You must be kidding!"

Charlie laughed. "Oh, I don't mean I won't be glad to be up and around. It's just that the routine, the work here, has been interesting."

The doctor applied a salve and placed a square of gauze over the wound. "It's hard work, Charlie, and not nearly as glamorous as some people think."

"I wasn't thinking about any glamor. It just seemed that there was a lot of, well, satisfaction in healing people."

The doctor expertly taped the bandage in place and pulled the bed sheet up. "Sure, there's satisfaction. But there's also a good bit of disappointment and a sizable share of frustration. We're virtually helpless in so many cases. There are so many diseases that still baffle us, even with all the knowledge we have. By the way, what are you going into when you graduate?"

Charlie clasped his hands behind his head, thinking back to that day when young Elsa died. "I've been sort of aiming at engineering, but now I'm not so sure. Maybe . . . maybe I'll try to get into medical school when I get my bachelor's degree."

The doctor made some notations on the chart and put it back on the hook at the foot of Charlie's bed. "It's a long road, son, and it's hard work every inch of the way." He smiled at his young patient. "But something tells me you're the sort who'll do whatever he sets out to do. Whatever you decide on, good luck to you. I'll be around to see you tomorrow and then we'll talk about getting you out of here."

Drew's feelings continued to drift more in the direction of medicine as a career. But his preoccupation was still with athletics. On Amherst's track team, Charlie was also a star. In the high hurdles he set records that stood for years. In his junior year he sustained another injury during a track meet, this time a painful ankle injury. It appeared that the team would be without him during a track meet against Brown University in Providence, Rhode Island. Charlie argued that he would be able to make the meet, but Coach Tuss McLaughry, putting the good of his boys ahead of winning, insisted that Charlie see a specialist in Boston.

"We'll let the doctor make the decision," the coach said. "If he puts you on the sidelines, Charlie, that's where you'll stay."

Brown had a fine track team, and the meet was going to be tough enough even if Drew was able to compete. Without him, Amherst's chances were virtually non-existent. He took the train to Boston a day ahead of the rest of the squad. The specialist examined the ankle injury carefully, took X rays, taped the ankle, then sat down at his desk while the young athlete watched him anxiously.

"How do you feel about competing?" the doctor asked.

"How do *I* feel?" Charlie echoed with his usual grin. "I feel like running from here to Providence if you give the word!"

The doctor smiled. "I thought so. All right, Drew, you can participate. But if the ankle gives you any trouble, you tell McLaughry, do you understand? If you take chances with that injury, it could mean no more athletic competition for you from now on. Don't try to be a hero."

Charlie stood up. "All right, sir. I'll take care."

When he reached the field on the Brown campus that afternoon, the meet was about to start. His friends gathered around him.

"How about it, Charlie?" said Bill Hastie. "What'd the doctor say?"

"He said take it easy."

"He must not have known he was talking to Charlie Drew," George Gilmer quipped.

From across the field one of the coaches called, "Charlie! Get dressed! Only five minutes before the shot put!"

Drew went on that afternoon to win the shot put, as well as taking first place in the broad jump and second in both the high jump and high hurdles. The other three Negro boys on the squad—Bill Hastie, Monty Cobb, and George Gilmer—did almost as well in their events. But Brown University managed to get more total points than Amherst and won the meet.

The Amherst squad took the loss in a sportsmanlike manner. They had all done their best, but the opposition had been better. Now they were looking forward to the banquet that night at the Narragansett Hotel.

Charlie and Monty Cobb were talking about the high-hurdle event as they came out of the dressing room and walked toward the cars that were to take them to the hotel. Hastie and Gilmer were in a group just behind them.

"If you hadn't tipped that last hurdle, Charlie," Monty Cobb was saying, "you'd have won it. . . ."

Drew stopped, looking curiously at the silent group standing around the cars. Several of the boys glanced toward him, then turned away as if embarrassed.

"Wonder what's wrong?" Charlie said.

The student manager was talking with one of the coaches in low tones. As Charlie and the others approached, the manager walked to meet them.

"Fellows," he started. "I don't know just how to put this, really. It's just that . . . well, the hotel people have contacted us and said they didn't know there were any . . ." He looked into the serious eyes of Charlie Drew and touched his lips with his tongue. "They didn't know there were any colored boys on our team. The hotel says it's against their policy to serve . . . colored people."

Charlie looked around at the somber faces of his teammates. His gaze stopped briefly on "Doc" Newport, the Negro trainer who had been with the Amherst team for many years. "What about 'Doc'?" he asked. "They've served him before."

The young manager shook his head glumly. "They say they can make an exception in his case. It's not as if he were a member of the team. I've checked every other hotel in town, and there just isn't any place that can serve a group this large on such short notice. Look" —his eyes flicked from Charlie to the other Negro athletes—"how about you fellows having dinner at the Commons here on campus?"

Charlie Drew looked around at his three companions. No one spoke. There was little they could say or do under the circumstances.

The rest of the squad went on to the hotel as planned. Charlie Drew, Monty Cobb, Bill Hastie, and George Gilmer walked across the Brown University campus to the Commons and had their dinner. The cars stopped later that evening to pick them up for the return trip to Amherst. It was a silent ride. But it was not the defeat on the field that caused it. The boys could take an honest loss such as that. It was what had happened afterward that hurt.

There were other times, though, that left a better feeling. A similar incident took place in a Boston hotel the following year. The Amherst team trooped into the lobby after the drive across the state from their college. As they milled about the registration desk, talking and laughing, the desk clerk saw Charlie and the other Negro players. He pursed his lips and shook his head.

"Sorry, we don't cater to colored people here. Hotel rule."

"But we've got reservations!" the student manager protested. "We've had them for weeks!"

The clerk shrugged. "Sorry, son. I don't make the rules, I just carry them out. Now, you white boys sign the register——"

Coach Tuss McLaughry, big, brusque, with the gait of a fullback, pushed through the group. "What's the trouble?" he boomed.

The desk clerk nodded toward the Negro boys.

"It's them, sir. I can't register colored people." Seeing the growing anger in the coach's eyes, the man put out both hands in a gesture of helplessness. "Now don't blame *me*. I just work here. It's a hotel rule."

Tuss McLaughry's jaw knotted, but he realized an argument would be unlikely to accomplish anything constructive. "All right," he said, making an effort to control his anger. "All right, you've got your rule, but Boston's got more than one hotel. Pick up your bags, boys," he thundered. "Let's go!"

As the team began to move across the lobby toward the door, the distraught clerk called out after McLaughry, "Hey! What about these reservations? We've been holding these rooms! You can't just—just walk out like this!"

People seated about the lobby were lowering their newspapers and watching curiously. The coach paused, turned on his heel, and pinned the man with a stony gaze. "Can't we? You just watch, mister!"

Charlie Drew's scholastic record at Amherst showed barely a glimmer of the scientific genius that was to develop later. But what he may have lacked in academic achievement went virtually unnoticed by his fellow students and alumni alike. He made the varsity track team each of his four years and was captain his senior year. Charlie was the only boy on the track team to win his varsity letter as a freshman, and he could almost always be counted on in any meet for the next four years to win two firsts and two seconds. His specialty was the 120-yard high hurdles. In his junior year he set a new college record for that event, and the following year, as captain of the Amherst track team, he won the National A.A.U. high-hurdle championship.

It was in football, though, that Charlie made his indelible mark at Amherst. Forty years later, Coach Tuss McLaughry, who was to go on to become coach at Dartmouth, as well as coaching for several years in the East-West Shrine games and several All-Star affairs, said, "As a football player, [Charlie] Drew was great. He could have played regular on any team in the country, both in his era and any time since. . . . [He had] tremendous speed and quick reactions, a great second effort, and was a splendid passer. He could hit a bull's-eye with the old ball at any distance up to fifty yards. Furthermore, he was a tiger on defense. When he tackled, the runner went down as though he were shot. Charlie Drew was the best player I ever coached."

Charlie Drew was, in the years 1922 to 1926 at Amherst, what might be called a BMOC—Big Man on Campus. A man with his athletic prowess could not help being something of a hero in the eyes of his fellow students, and his personality added to it. He was good-humored, frank, and completely without vanity.

Yet the fact that he was a Negro undoubtedly played a major role in his not being chosen captain of the football team his senior year. There was also a student group on campus, Scarab, made up supposedly of the dozen or so seniors who were best known for their all-round achievement. Scarab chose its own successors each year. It was done, dramatically, late in the spring quarter, with the outgoing Scarab members walking into morning chapel and tapping their successors. Drew was an obvious candidate, but after several men had been tapped and Charlie passed by, it also became obvious to most of the student body that he had not been chosen. Gradually, with only a few boys at first, there began a chant: *"Drew! Drew! Drew!"* As the last of the new Scarab members was named—Drew omitted—the chant filled the auditorium.

Oddly, Charlie himself appeared not to have any of the bitterness his friends felt at this slight.

He did not finish his college career without honors, however. In addition to the captaincy of the track squad, Charlie won the Pentathlon Trophy all four years, the Mossman Trophy upon graduation for having been the athlete who brought the greatest honor to his school, and honorable mention on the All-American football squad in 1926.

But the most important thing resulting from his undergraduate days at Amherst came out in a conversation as Charlie and Bill Hastie walked across the campus on a warm afternoon in May, a few weeks before graduation. Hastie had decided to go on to law school. He turned to Drew as they talked.

"Have you made up your mind, Charlie? I mean about what you're going to do after graduation?"

Drew nodded. "I've decided to go to medical school."

5 A New Day at Morgan College

While Charlie was charging his way to football fame and earning his bachelor's degree from Amherst, a new sister, Eva, had arrived at the Drew household back in Washington. Nora and Richard Drew decided to move away from the humid, unhealthy area of Foggy Bottom for the sake of the baby. They went across the Potomac into Virginia where they bought a modest two-story house in Arlington, which, in the early twenties, was virtually open country.

Medical school for Charlie was now going to have to wait. Even though his scholarship had paid most of his tuition at Amherst and the jobs he held had helped with additional expenses, Charlie had found it necessary to go into debt to complete his four years of college. Now, with the added expense of payments on the house in Arlington, his father was not able to offer anything but the most meager financial help. Medical school was an expensive undertaking, so Charlie began to look around for a job that would allow him to pay off his debts and put away some money toward the years of medical study.

His football career had made him known, and several offers of coaching jobs came in. One in particular appealed to him. It came from Morgan College, a small church-affiliated Negro school in Baltimore, Maryland. The position was that of athletic director and instructor in chemistry and biology in the academy, or lower school.

Not long after receiving his diploma from Amherst, Charlie Drew was sitting in the office of Dr. John Spencer, the president of Morgan College. Before him, Dr. Spencer had Drew's record from Amherst, as well as letters of recommendation, including one from Coach Tuss McLaughry.

"I think you're just the sort of man we need, Mr. Drew," Dr. Spencer said. "We can offer you a salary of fifteen hundred dollars a year, and quarters in one of our dormitories, Belle View Hall."

"There's one thing, Dr. Spencer——" Charlie started.

"The salary? I'm afraid it's all our budget will stand."

"No, sir, the salary's just fine. And I'd like to accept

the position, but I couldn't do it without telling you at the outset I can't stay more than two years."

The college president pursed his lips. "Then you don't plan teaching or coaching as a career? You've got your sights set on something else?"

Drew decided to be completely frank. "It's possible I may get into teaching again one day, but my plan, as soon as I can afford it, is to go to medical school."

"That's certainly commendable. And it's also commendable of you to tell me this."

"Will this interfere with my taking the position?"

Dr. Spencer shook his head. "No, Mr. Drew." The school president picked up a letter from his desk. "On the whole your grades at Amherst were little better than average. But you did very well in biology and chemistry, and Coach McLaughry gives you his highest recommendation for the position of athletic director." Dr. Spencer smiled. "The title may be a bit presumptuous, Mr. Drew. But with only budget enough for one man, why not give him the advantage of the title?"

The years from 1926 to 1928 were to reveal another side of a many-faceted Charles Richard Drew. Until he took the job of athletic director at Morgan College, coaching duties there had been handled on a part-time basis by coaches from other schools in the Baltimore area.

The dormitory—Belle View—had been the home of the previous owner of the land. When the college acquired the property, the huge house and other buildings had been converted to school purposes. It was here in Belle View that Charlie and another young instructor were in charge of the thirty-five boys who also occupied the house, most of them members of one or more of the athletic squads.

Almost from the beginning, the boys were dedicated to the young coach. One boy in particular, Daniel "Pinky" Clark, who was perhaps the best natural athlete in the school at the time, was preparing to take an athletic scholarship to another school in the fall of 1926. Pinky lived in Belle View, and on the day that Morgan College was to play its first game of the '26 season, he was in his room packing his belongings. Charlie Drew needed him in the quarterback position, and needed him badly. Drew mounted the stairs from his first-floor room and stopped at Clark's open door.

"Well, Pinky, it's going to be tough without you," he said.

Pinky Clark looked up from what he was doing. "Amherst is going to find it tough going without *you* this year, Coach."

Drew laughed. "I don't know about that. The thing is, I had to leave. You don't."

"Sure, but you can't really blame me, can you? I mean, where I'm going the team is better. Morgan's barely in the prep-school class, Coach, and you know it."

Drew nodded and sauntered in to sit on the edge of the bed. "That's where the challenge is. Let's bring it out of the prep-school class."

Clark folded a pair of trousers and placed them in the suitcase. "Did you know that Morgan College has never scored a touchdown against Howard University? Not even *one?*"

"Then let's score one. If we can't do it this year, then next year. You can help us do it, Pinky. Oh, we might be able to do it without you, but we'd rather have you with us."

By the time the talk was over, Pinky Clark had begun to unpack his bags. Half an hour later he was going over the plays with Coach Drew, and that afternoon, with scarcely a hundred students looking on, quarterback Pinky Clark and the Morgan eleven went out and lost their first game under their new coach.

Morgan College had been expected to lose. The school was a member of the CIAA—Colored Intercollegiate Athletic Association (now the Central Intercollegiate Athletic Association)—which included colleges such as Howard University, Lincoln, Hampton, and others which were four or five times larger than Morgan and consequently more attractive to young athletes coming up from high school. But the loss was not like those of previous years. The presence of the new coach saw to that. Charlie Drew commended his team on its showing and immediately set their sights for the next game.

Slowly, the ragtag squad began to shape up. Every afternoon there was practice and a blackboard session to sharpen up the plays. There was only a rocky, open field on the Morgan campus, and some of the home games were played there. Others were played in south Baltimore at the "Black Sox" stadium.

The small student body began to take more interest in the games, and Coach Drew organized cheerleaders to heighten the school pride. Late in his first season, Morgan was playing Lincoln at Black Sox stadium. Morgan College still had to win its first game, though several had been close. The crowd in the stands was the biggest that had turned out, and the game was fought hard. The score was tied, 6 to 6, and there were only minutes to play. Morgan had the ball, and quarterback Pinky Clark called the signals, dropped back with the ball, and flipped a pass into the flats to end "Marse" Hill. He grabbed the ball, and, completely in the clear, began to streak down the sidelines toward the goal. The Morgan students were on their feet in the stands, screaming. Then, suddenly, a blanket-wrapped figure leaped off the Lincoln bench and, with a perfect flying tackle, brought the galloping Hill to earth. Bedlam broke out. Players and spectators swarmed onto the field, and it was several minutes before order could be restored.

The officials ruled a touchdown for Morgan, and Coach Charlie Drew was carried out of the stadium on the shoulders of his players. The first flashes of a long tradition at Morgan were beginning to show.

Charles Drew, true to form, pursued his work with complete dedication. His ability to inspire the team as a coach was just as remarkable as it had been as a player for Amherst. "Every stand is a goal-line stand," he would tell the boys before each game, and they would go onto the field and play it exactly that way. Morgan, being the smallest school in its league, was almost invariably overpowered by the opposition, but under Charlie Drew the team was never a pushover. For the first time, the long neglected victory column began to receive some attention.

One longed for goal was achieved in 1927 in a game against Howard University in Washington. At the end of the third quarter, it seemed that the jinx of never having scored against the Washingtonians was going to continue to plague Morgan. The score was 24–0, even though the boys from Morgan made the opponent fight for every inch gained. The game was a rough one, and suddenly, as a Howard runner was hit by Morgan tacklers, the ball popped loose. There was a mad scramble for it. Then a long-legged Morgan guard, W.L.D. Light, appeared with the pigskin clutched tightly under one arm. He raced down the field and across the goal for the first touchdown ever scored against Howard, bringing his school a moral if not actual victory.

At the end of the game students poured onto the field in a free-for-all. Charlie Drew herded his players toward the dressing room, but quarterback Pinky Clark doubled back to join the fray. As the Morgan College star leaped into the battle, he suddenly felt a pair of powerful arms encircle him from behind. Twisting and struggling, he glanced over his shoulder into the calm eyes of his coach.

Charlie Drew shook his head. "Not today, Pinky," he said. "Not today, boy. The team stays out of this. We did all right. Remember what I told you last year? Well, we did it. We scored against Howard. Let's be satisfied for now with that."

Clark's thoughts went back to the day Drew had talked him into staying on at Morgan. He laughed. "Sure, Coach. We did do it, didn't we!"

Together, they walked away from the student battle and down into the locker room.

Charlie Drew taught his biology and chemistry classes in Washington Hall, and when football season was over, began to coach both a boys' and girls' basketball team. The home games were played in a building known simply as the Stone Barn, a carry-over from the time when the grounds were under private ownership. Both these squads fell under Drew's spell, just as the football squad had. Many of the football players, notably Pinky Clark, became basketball stars as well. A good track team was developed in the spring, and even though there was no track on campus, this did not deter Coach Drew, who trained his runners by sprints up and down Hillen Avenue, which ran alongside the Morgan College campus.

All the time he was putting away every dollar he could manage from his salary, getting ready for the future. It was a slow process, but the debts at Amherst were paid off, and his bank balance began to rise.

In the summer of 1927, he returned to Washington and worked as manager at the Francis Swimming Pool with his brother Joe Drew under him as one of the life-guards, and once again, when fall came, he went back to his duties at Morgan College.

Drew's brilliant start as coach the previous year had brought an unexpected bonus to the school. For the first time, alumni interest was aroused in the athletic program. The school pride was beginning to spread beyond the campus. By the time the football season came to a close—with the greatest success in the history of the college—Charlie Drew was clearly recognized as the man who had achieved the impossible. What had been little more than a sandlot gang throwing and kicking a ball around, was now a well-drilled, proud team. Even their most powerful foes—Howard and Lincoln—no longer began a game with Morgan assuming an easy victory.

After a faculty meeting in the late winter of 1928, Dr. Spencer and the college registrar, Edward Wilson, approached Drew.

"Charlie," the president began, "we want you to stay on after this year. Ed and I want you, the regents want you, the alumni want you, and not least, the student body wants you."

Drew had anticipated something like this. Still, it was hard to turn down, even though his mind had long been made up about the future.

"What I said when I took the job will have to stand, Dr. Spencer," he said. "It's been a wonderful experience for me, working with you and the school, but . . ." He shrugged.

"A pay raise has been authorized, Charlie," Ed Wilson said, "but I don't suppose that would influence you."

"I'm afraid not, Ed. I guess I'm bullheaded, but I've decided on medicine and not coaching as a career."

Wilson smiled and put one hand on Charlie's shoulder. "None of us really expected you to change your mind, Charlie. But we had to try."

In May, Charlie Drew sent his application to Howard University Medical School. This had been his intent all along, and he anticipated no difficulty in being admitted for the class that was to begin the following September. But the unexpected happened. A few weeks later he found an envelope waiting when he got back to his quarters in Belle View Hall. The return address was Howard University, and Drew eagerly opened it. Inside were the transcripts of his Amherst record and a letter from the registrar of the medical school. It stated, regretfully, that Drew's English credits at Amherst were insufficient for admission to Howard University Medical School, and the application, therefore, had to be rejected.

Drew slumped down at the desk, stunned. With all his careful planning, his working as coach and instructor for two years, saving money in every possible way in order to accumulate a bank account to help carry him through the long years of study that lay ahead, this was the one thing he had not anticipated.

He read the brief letter through again. He had never thought of any other medical school, and now he had been turned down by Howard.

There was a tap at the door. "Coach?" It was Pinky Clark, and peering in, he saw the expression on Drew's face and the letter in his hand. "Anything wrong? Not bad news, is it?"

"Bad news . . . ?" Drew tossed the letter on the desk. "No, Pinky, just a bit unexpected."

The young athlete grinned. "Good. About time for dinner. You coming?"

"Sure, I'll be right along."

He picked up the letter, folded it, and put it into his pocket, then walked to the window. Late afternoon shadows slanted across the campus. Students trudged toward the dining hall, talking and laughing among themselves. Maybe it was a good thing that he hadn't officially resigned his position yet, Drew thought. This certainly put a different light on the immediate future. English credits . . . strange how that could have happened.

He looked around at the clock on the desk. It was almost six, but if he hurried he might be able to catch Ed Wilson before he left his office.

Drew strode quickly across the campus. The registrar was just closing the door when the young coach arrived. He could see immediately that something was wrong.

"What is it, Charlie? Haven't you heard from Howard yet?"

Drew took the letter from his pocket. "I've heard from them, all right," he said glumly. "Read this."

Wilson opened the letter, read it, then with a shake of his head handed it back. "What are you going to do?"

"I want you to send copies of my Amherst transcript to other schools. Howard isn't the only medical school in the country."

"I kind of figured you wouldn't be throwing in the towel." Wilson unlocked the door. "Come on, let's get them out right now."

Drew listed half a dozen schools, among them Ohio State, University of Michigan, and McGill University, in Montreal, Canada.

Ed Wilson went over the list, then looked at his friend. "Would you rather I try to clear up this English credit business with Howard before we do this? Your credits were sufficient to get your Bachelor's degree from Amherst. It seems to me——"

"No. Let's send these out and see what happens," Drew insisted.

"All right." Wilson took the cover off the typewriter. "Let's get started."

A week dragged by. There was no reply as yet from the medical schools, but on Friday afternoon "Hoss" Spalding, who in later years was to become head of Morgan's chemistry department, brought a letter to Drew's room. "Something for you, Coach, from Howard University."

Drew took the envelope and looked at the return address curiously. Could it be that a mistake had been made in rejecting his application? Quickly he tore the envelope open. It was not from the medical school, but from the Howard University Athletic Department. The frown on Drew's face changed slowly as his eyes went down the page. By the time he had finished the letter, there was the trace of a smile on his lips and a twinkle in his eye.

"Hoss" Spalding, like everyone else, had got wind of the rejection by Howard. He cleared his throat. "Good news this time, Coach?"

Charlie Drew laughed and dropped the letter on the desk. "They've offered me a job as an instructor in the athletic department!"

That night Drew wrote a carefully worded reply to the offer, to the effect that if his English credits were insufficient to allow him the privilege of becoming a student at Howard, they most certainly must be woefully inadequate to allow him to assume a position on the faculty, and therefore he regretfully had to decline the post offered.

A few days later, the first of the replies to his inquiries to other schools began to come in. Each of them stated that Drew's academic record was good enough to meet their requirements. The last to arrive—from McGill, in Montreal—included an application form.

"They're all top schools, Charlie," Ed Wilson told him. "The fact is, your being turned down by Howard might have been a blessing in disguise."

Drew nodded thoughtfully as he shuffled through the letters. They *were* all good schools, but the one in Canada had an appeal he had not thought of before. Even in the so-called "enlightened" New England states, he and the other Negroes on the Amherst team had run into numerous incidents involving race. Drew had heard stories of Canadian schools, of how equality was not just a word, but a reality.

He pulled the letter from among the others and read it over. There was no mention of race anywhere in it or on the application. He nodded slowly, making his decision. "This is the one, Ed. McGill. That's where I want to study medicine. May I use your typewriter? I'd like to get this application form in the next mail."

Wilson looked at his young friend and laughed. "Certainly, Charlie. Help yourself!"

The departure in the summer of 1928 of Coach Charlie Drew was a sad day for Morgan College. He had literally pulled Morgan's athletic program up by its bootstraps and had created the start of a tradition in athletics there. He was leaving behind the nucleus of a fine football team for a school as small as Morgan. The track, baseball, and basketball teams were well-drilled and always in contention.

Charle Drew was not a man Morgan College, or the men he worked with, would forget.

6 Medical School in Canada

At the age of twenty-four, with two successful careers already behind him, Charlie Drew came home to Washington. He lived with his family in Arlington and worked again as manager of the Francis Pool in the capital. He had saved every dollar possible from his salary as coach at Morgan College, and to this nest egg he added what he could from his summer job. Even so, he was well aware of the expense that lay ahead during the five-year medical course at McGill.

His father assured him of whatever financial help he might manage, but with the new house and three other children, two of whom were in school and the third, little Eva, only a year away from enrollment, Charlie knew his father would be hard pressed without the added burden of sending money to Canada.

"I'll get a part-time job when I get to Montreal," he assured him. "The same as I did at Amherst."

"You'll make it, son," Richard Drew said confidently. "It takes drive, and you've got plenty of that."

The summer passed swiftly, and on a day late in August, Charlie stood on the platform of a train and waved good-bye to his family and friends. As the train sped northward, the young man gazed out at the countryside. The coach wheels click-clacked hypnotically along the rails. Dr. Charles Richard Drew, he thought. Would that day ever come?

The train thundered on through the night. A Pullman berth was a luxury Charlie Drew could do without. He slept soundly and well sitting up in the day-coach, and when he awoke, the first bright rays of the sun were slanting in from the window across the aisle.

"Sleep good, young fellow?"

Charlie looked up to see the conductor. "Never slept better." He grinned, stretching.

"Lot of folks can't sleep at all in the coaches, but it didn't seem to bother you."

"I guess I'm just lucky that way," Charlie replied. "Sometimes a five-minute nap seems to do me as much good as eight hours' sleep."

The conductor sat down opposite him. "So you're headed for Montreal, huh? Got a job up there?"

Charlie shook his head. "I'm going to school. Medical school, at McGill University. This is my first year."

The conductor's expression didn't change, but the pause told Charlie what he was thinking. You didn't see many young Negroes going to medical school in Canada or anywhere else. "Well," he said after a moment, "you've got a long road ahead of you, and from what I hear, a hard one." The railroad man pulled out a watch and peered at it. "About six hours, and we'll be there." He got up and started down the aisle.

That afternoon, the train crossed a long bridge over the St. Lawrence River, and a few minutes later chugged to a halt at Windsor Station. Montreal, on the last day of August, was as hot and humid as Washington when Charlie Drew mounted the steps of the terminal and walked out into the sunlight of the city that was to be his home for the next seven years. A piece of luggage in each hand, the young man walked across Dominion Square and sat down on a bench amid the trees and the unemployed. The brooding length of Mount Royal lay a mile to the northwest. Along the curb of Rue Windsor the barkers of sightseeing buses made their spiels for the newly arrived passengers, while the drivers of horse-drawn *calèches* competed loudly for the business. In a great many ways the city reminded him of Washington as he picked up his bags and made his way up Rue Metcalfe toward the McGill campus.

As a freshman in medical school, Charlie Drew put

himself wholeheartedly into his studies. There had been signs of exceptional ability before, but this now became a constant flame rather than an occasional flash. Somehow, even with the heavy load of courses in anatomy, chemistry, bacteriology, and many others, Drew found time to engage in athletics and to get a job waiting on tables in order to supplement his savings.

But things were far from smooth. He had confidence in himself, in his ability to absorb the complexities of medical training, but there was always that specter of financial failure haunting him. The great Depression of the early 1930's fell over America like a pall, and the little aid that reached him from home dwindled to a trickle and at last stopped. Charlie managed to hang on to his job waiting on tables, but even that was jeopardized. During his second year at McGill, he wrote to his former coach at Amherst—Tuss McLaughry—and mentioned that an old football injury was causing him a great deal of pain, especially when he was required to stand for long periods of time, and he was fearful of having to give up his job because of this.

McLaughry, who was then coach at Brown University, wrote back at once telling him to hang on until he could get help. Completely unknown to Charlie, McLaughry immediately contacted a number of Drew's former classmates, informing them of his predicament. In a matter of days several hundred dollars had been rounded up, and McLaughry sent it on to Charlie in the form of a loan. He knew his former backfield star would not accept it as charity. Charlie was able to pay his board for quite some time in advance, and another crisis was passed. Some years later, when he had received his degree and was once more earning money, he sent Tuss McLaughry a check for the full amount.

Among the many friends Charlie made at McGill was a young English doctor, John Beattie, who taught bacteriology in the medical school.

Almost a head shorter than Drew, the wiry Englishman was first drawn to the young American by a mutual interest in sports. Charlie took several courses under Beattie, and the student-teacher relationship quickly grew into friendship.

One day in the fall of 1930, as Charlie was passing the door to Beattie's office, the Englishman called out to him.

"Charlie, have you seen the newspaper this morning?"

"Now where would I get the money to buy a newspaper, John?" Drew asked wryly. "Or the time to read it?"

Beattie motioned to him. "Come on in."

Charlie shifted his notebook and stepped into the small, book-crammed room. There was a newspaper on Beattie's desk, and the Englishman picked it up and held it out. An article had been circled. "The Nobel prize in medicine was awarded yesterday," he said.

Charlie took the paper and read the caption. *Landsteiner Takes Nobel Medicine Prize.* He looked up. "He's the second American to win a Nobel prize this year. Sinclair Lewis was awarded the literature prize."

Beattie sat down. "Be fair, Charlie. Karl Landsteiner was an Austrian when he did the work that won the Nobel prize." There was a twinkle in Beattie's eye. "He became an American citizen just last year."

"The discovery of blood groups," Charlie mused. "When was it he published his findings—1900?"

"That's right. Thirty years ago. And there's no way of guessing how many people have died since that time because Landsteiner's discoveries weren't put to clinical use."

"I don't suppose there's anything particularly unusual about that," Drew said. "New ideas aren't accepted easily. When William Harvey published his theory on the circulation of blood in the seventeenth century, he was ridiculed."

"I suppose that's one of the frustrations of being at the frontier, Charlie," John Beattie said seriously. He gazed out the window at the cold Canadian sky. "Still, there's a fascination in research that can't be found anywhere else. You're out there in the very front, blazing the trail. You know, I've been thinking about it for quite some time. When I go back to England, that's what I'm going to get into. Research. Even with a man of Landsteiner's genius in the field, there's an awful lot left to be done in blood." He turned. "What is this? Your third year here?"

"That's right."

"Well, you've a long way yet to go. Two years after

this, then internship and residency. You're bright, Charlie. Very bright. I've heard the dean say the same thing. You ought to give a bit of thought to something along those lines."

"Research?" Charlie said. "I have thought about it."

"For some reason I can't explain, I can't see you in private practice," Beattie said.

"There are other things. Look at you, for instance. What's wrong with teaching?"

"Wrong?" Beattie said with a laugh. "Nothing! But for me it doesn't have the challenge presented by research."

"But it does for me," Charlie said. "It's very hard for a young Negro to get a first-rate medical education. You talk of frontiers, John. There's a frontier in itself."

The conversation with Beattie lingered in Drew's mind. In addition to his regular studies, he now began to delve into books on blood. That same year, because of his excellent record, he was awarded a scholarship, and for the first time since arriving at McGill, found himself able to give up his outside job. The additional time was devoted to even more concentration on his studies.

But Charlie Drew had not retired to the laboratory and the library. He went out for the track team, which in Canada, unlike the United States, was open to graduate students as well as undergraduates. Just as at

Amherst, he was a star, and he set several Canadian records. His fourth year, he was elected captain of the track team.

No doubt Charles Drew's excellent physical condition contributed to the stamina which marked his entire life. Once he had set upon a goal, he seemed to have the strength of more than one man in driving himself toward it. The attainment of his medical degree was his present concern, and he led his class. His academic record was excellent, and as one of the top three men in his senior class, he became a member of Alpha Omega Alpha Honorary Medical Society, as well as winning one of the most coveted honors open to seniors, the J. Francis Williams Fellowship.

On a bright, sunny day in May, 1933, only a week before his twenty-ninth birthday, Charles Richard Drew, in the traditional cap and gown, had conferred upon him the degrees of Doctor of Medicine and Master of Surgery.

Dr. John Beattie was one of the first to shake his hand after the ceremony was over. "Congratulations, Charlie," he said heartily. "They won't forget you soon up here!"

"I'm not leaving, John," Drew said as they walked along beneath the maples. "I'm interning at Montreal General Hospital."

Charlie went home to Washington to spend a few weeks with his family. The situation there was not good. His father had lost his job, or more accurately, there had simply been no demand in the carpet business, and his employers found themselves in no position to keep him on. Thousands of unemployed people spent the warm days of summer in the parks of the capital. It had been the same in Montreal, but the effect was somehow more devastating to see those he knew in such a predicament.

Richard Drew tried to show his old cheer and enthusiasm, but it was difficult, and his son could see the effort. It was with a heavy heart that Charlie returned to Montreal to begin his internship at Montreal General. Out of his almost non-existent pay as an interne, he managed to send everything he could back home.

At Montreal General, Charlie spent his first six months in a rotating internship—spending several weeks in various hospital services such as pediatrics, obstetrics, internal medicine, and so on. Later, he concentrated on his specialty, surgery. With other interns, he had a room in the hospital and was on call night and day. Whenever he could find the time, he dropped by the pathology laboratory where Dr. John Beattie had an area devoted to blood-typing for transfusions. It was a rudimentary setup—a small refrigerating unit, microscope, slides, a bottle of saline solution to prevent clotting of the blood samples, and a row of test tubes.

The danger inherent in blood transfusions had been reduced immensely by the application of Karl Landsteiner's discovery of blood groups. Still, there were unexpected reactions, even deaths, that baffled the doctors.

Often the time factor involved could mean life or death to the patient. When it was known well ahead of an operation that blood would be needed, the patient's blood would be typed in the laboratory, and donors would be arranged for. The donors generally were friends or relatives who had the same blood type as the patient, or there might be professional donors, or even hospital staff members.

But in emergency cases it was often a different matter. A person critically injured, suffering shock and loss of blood, could very well die in the time needed to carry out the arrangements for transfusion. First, there was the typing of the patient's blood, then the seeking out of a donor. When the donor was found, another half hour or so elapsed while the blood was drawn, then the bottle rushed into the operating room. With luck, the patient might be saved. Without it, the balance could tip the other way.

Working in the laboratory one afternoon with Beattie, Charlie shook his head and sighed. He was thinking of a young woman who had been brought into the emergency ward the night before. She had been involved in an automobile accident in which the driver had been killed. By the time she was freed from the wreckage and brought into the hospital, she was in shock and had lost a great deal of blood.

"John," Charlie said, "there has got to be some way developed so that blood can be preserved and stored, ready for immediate use."

Beattie had been on duty when the girl was

brought in, and he sensed this was on his friend's mind. "The girl who was in the wreck? She died?"

Drew nodded his head grimly. "I think she might have lived if we'd been able to give her blood quicker than we did. Think what it would mean if we could have typed her blood and gone straight to a supply, typed and ready to transfuse."

Beattie took a medical journal from a drawer. "Dr. Bethune showed me an article today. I think it'll interest you."

Drew took the journal and began to read. It was about experiments a Russian doctor had been conducting, mixing cadaver blood with a sodium citrate solution that kept it from clotting. "That's very interesting," Drew said when he had finished. "But there's still the problem of the breakdown of the red cells."

The door opened suddenly, and one of the other interns peered in. "You're wanted in surgery, Charlie! They'll be needing blood, and quick!"

Minutes later, Drew entered the operating room. Masked and gowned doctors and nurses worked over a young man on the operating table. At a word from the surgeon, Charlie quickly took a sample of blood for testing and hurried back to the lab. He and Beattie typed it first by Landsteiner's original method and then by a second method to be absolutely certain of the type.

"It's my type," Drew said. He rolled up his sleeve. "Here, John, get busy."

It was not the first time Charlie had given his own

blood. Most of the interns and residents had had their blood typed and the information filed for just such emergencies.

Later that year Charlie said good-bye to his friend John Beattie. The Englishman was returning to his homeland. "Keep in touch," Beattie said as they shook hands. "Let me know what you decide to get into, Charlie."

In the months that followed, while Drew was finishing his internship and beginning his final year at Montreal General as a resident in surgery, the problem was often on Drew's mind. He was pulled strongly toward teaching, but there was also the field of research and the possibility of entering private practice.

His initial decision to teach rather than practice medicine was one that was not easily achieved. After so many years of deprivation to reach his first goal—that of becoming a doctor—the temptation to go into private practice must have been great. There was opportunity for an able surgeon in Canada, the barriers of racial discrimination being infinitely less than those below the border. Practicing in his own country would have been financially rewarding, yet Charles Drew felt drawn toward teaching. In December of 1934, as he was beginning his last six months as resident in surgery at Montreal General Hospital, he wrote to his friend, Dr. Montague Cobb, who had just joined the teaching staff at Howard Medical School. He asked many questions about the conditions there and concluded his letter by saying, "No, Monty, I am not about to apply for the job of professor, at least not yet, but I should like to have an idea of the setup there, so that I might bear it in mind in my further training."

Changes had been taking place at Howard. A new dean of the medical school, Dr. Numa P.G. Adams, had taken office in 1929, and a program of rebuilding and strengthening the medical faculty had been begun. The outstanding record made by Drew at McGill was well-known to Dean Adams, and when Drew's residency at Montreal General was completed in the summer of 1935, correspondence between him and Dean Adams culminated in an appointment for Drew as instructor in pathology at Howard.

And so, almost seven years after coming to Montreal as a first-year medical student, Dr. Charles Richard Drew boarded a train in cavernous Windsor Station, and headed south for Washington.

7 The Lamp of Learning

As Charles Richard Drew finished his training in Canada in 1935, the world was once more on the verge of war. Adolf Hitler had unilaterally rejected the Treaty of Versailles, and factories in the industrial Ruhr and Rhineland belched smoke night and day while Germany went about the business of rearmament. The Fuehrer decreed universal military conscription in the Third Reich, aiming at an army of half a million men. Meanwhile, Hermann Goering announced that a German Air Force had already been built.

Across the Atlantic, the United States, under President Franklin Delano Roosevelt, struggled to extricate itself from the Great Depression. The inability of Richard Drew to find work—not simply in his trade as carpet layer, but any sort of work—had a debilitating effect on him. An illness developed into pneumonia, and although his doctor-son had hurried home from Montreal, the elder Drew was beyond help.

The death of his father had a profound effect on Charlie Drew. If any doubt still lingered concerning his future course, this had a part in settling it. He would do whatever he could to advance his race, and to Drew this meant going on to Howard to teach. The Negro was far behind in American medicine. The important men in the profession, in Drew's mind, still looked on Negro physicians as country doctors capable of little more than watching over the sick and poor of their race. It was this point of view that Charlie Drew wanted to change, and education was the way to do it.

At Howard Medical School, Drew assumed his new duties at a salary of $150 a month. He had actually made almost as much many years ago as an enterprising twelve-year-old with a tightly organized newspaper sales force. But Charlie's sights were not set on moneymaking. The work at Howard was challenging, and he put all his vast energy into it.

One of the goals at Howard Medical School was to begin a program of surgical resident training at Freedmen's Hospital, the crumbling Negro facility across the street from the college. There was no medical school or hospital in the country at that time which would accept young Negroes for clinical training, and Dean Numa Adams went to the American Medical Association's Council on Medical Education and Hospitals and got approval for a resident training program at Howard.

This was a giant stride forward, and another step was taken the following year when the Rockefeller Foundation came to realize the plight of the Negro in regard to medical education. The eminent Dr. Edward L. Howes, of Yale College of Medicine, was sent to Howard by the Foundation for a five-year period as Professor of Surgery.

Under Dr. Howes, Charlie Drew moved from instructor in pathology to assistant in surgery. Howes was a man of great confidence and control, while at the same time often abrupt in his comments. One morning at Freedmen's Hospital, after observing an operation, Howes asked the surgeon who had performed it how he justified the particular procedure he had used.

"I've been doing the operation this way for fifteen years," the surgeon replied.

Howes did not mince words. "Did it ever occur to you that you have been doing it wrong for fifteen years!" he snapped.

Howes was a highly respected man among both his fellow faculty members and the residents. Though his manner at times was brusque and even caustic, he was quick to recognize talent, and he saw this in the young surgeon, Charles Drew.

Howes watched his young colleague carefully,

and in the spring of 1938, he discussed an idea with Dean Adams. The result was a letter to the Rockefeller Foundation's General Education Board in New York.

A week later two doctors sat in a book-cluttered office high in the vast complex of New York's Columbia-Presbyterian Medical Center. One of the men was Dr. Allen O. Whipple, professor of surgery at Columbia University's medical school. The other, Dr. John Scudder, a tall, intense young physician, was research director of the Center. Only a few years back from six years of missionary medicine in India, Scudder was deeply interested in new concepts of fluid and electrolytic therapy in the treatment of shock.

Dr. Whipple picked up a letter from amongst the papers on his desk. "We've come across a very promising young man who might fit into one of your research programs, John," he said. "Took his M.D. and C.M. degrees at McGill. Top honors, a very bright fellow. Presently he's at Howard, in Washington." He pushed the letter across the desk. "This is from Dr. Edward Howes who's heading up the surgery department there under a Foundation grant. Both Howes and Dean Numa Adams are very keen on this man and on the opportunity a fellowship here would afford a Negro surgeon."

John Scudder glanced at the letter, and frowning slightly, leaned back and took a battered pipe from his pocket. A Negro doctor, he thought. Even though certain facilities were not marked "colored" or "white" in

New York, as they were in the South, racial segregation was very much a fact. In a group of researchers who, of necessity, had to work very closely together, he wondered where mere personal inconvenience would end and actual barriers might arise. There were quite enough problems without adding to them.

He packed tobacco into the pipe, struck a match, and drew the flame down into the bowl. Looking once more at the letter, he lowered it onto the desk. "Howes is certainly sold on him, no doubt about that."

"But you think the racial implications would be a hindrance?"

"Don't you?"

Whipple smiled at his young colleague. "Possibly. But I know you well enough, John, to know that you wouldn't let anything of the sort stand in the way of putting a talented and deserving man on your team."

Scudder chuckled. "One more challenge, is that it?"

"It's your decision. What do you say?"

Scudder looked again at the name. "Dr. Charles Richard Drew . . ." He took a puff on his pipe. "Tell Howes to send him up."

Dr. Montague Cobb caught up with his friend in the long gloomy corridor outside the second floor wards at Freedmen's Hospital. "Charlie, Dean Adams wants to see you. Right away, in his office."

Drew glanced around, puzzled. "At nine in the morning? What's up?"

"Dr. Howes is with him. I've got a hunch about it, but I'll wait. You'd better get over there."

Drew shrugged. "Maybe I'm being fired, Monty." He turned and strode toward the stairwell.

At Dean Numa Adams' office in the administration building, Drew was not kept waiting. He was ushered inside, where he found both the dean and Dr. Howes.

"Sit down, Charlie," Howes said.

Drew looked from one man to the other. There was a definite feeling of excitement in the room as he slowly sank down on a chair.

"Charlie," Dr. Howes went on, "we've just gotten word regarding a request we made to the General Education Board of the Rockefeller Foundation." His eyes twinkled. "How would you like to spend a couple of years at Columbia-Presbyterian on a fellowship?"

"How would I——" Drew exclaimed, coming to his feet.

Dean Adams spoke. "It'll be tough going. You'd be working in a research program in addition to your surgery, and the pay is hardly worth mentioning."

"What sort of research?" he wanted to know.

"Have you heard of Dr. John Scudder?"

Drew nodded. "I've read a few things of his. Shock treatment."

"He's also interested in blood research, and he's Research Director at the Center."

Drew's eyes widened, and Dr. Howes said, "I thought that would strike a spark. Well, what do you say?"

"What do I say?" Charlie Drew grinned, the familiar feeling of excitement kindling inside him. "I say, when does the next train leave for New York?"

The dean rose and extended his hand to the young surgeon. "Congratulations, Dr. Drew. I don't think we could have found a better man for this opportunity."

It was not simply a personal chance for himself. Drew was well aware of this. It was a move forward for Negro physicians, and he had had the good fortune of being chosen to take the first step. Five days later, on a sweltering hot day in June, thirty-four-year-old Dr. Charles Richard Drew stood beside a subway kiosk on West 168th Street in New York City and gazed at the massive complex of buildings that comprised Columbia-Presbyterian Medical Center. Freedmen's Hospital—or as Howard's president, Mordecai Johnson once called it, "this Jim Crow shack"—would be lost in one of the Center's vast corridors.

Drew walked eagerly into the main building and asked directions to Dr. Scudder's office. At Scudder's floor, he found the place a beehive of activity. Doctors and technicians moved in and out of the gleaming laboratories, paying no attention to the newcomer. Research in medicine had long since passed the days of a lone doctor patiently gathering information. Harvey, Malpighi, Jenner—they would have been astounded at the sight that greeted Charles Drew on that day in 1938.

A secretary arranged for a desk in the corridor

outside Scudder's office, and there Drew waited for several days before an appointment could be arranged with the research director.

"Sorry I wasn't able to get around to you sooner, Dr. Drew," Scudder apologized as he greeted the young surgeon. "As you can see, we're pretty busy around here."

"It's quite a change from Freedmen's," Drew said. "We're busy there, of course, but with facilities like these we could——" He broke off smiling. "Perhaps someday."

"Well, you've got two years ahead of you here. Have you been giving any thought to what you might like to do in the way of research?"

"Frankly, I've had an interest in blood since my days at McGill. I've read something of your recent work, Dr. Scudder."

Scudder's expression brightened. "Oh? Well, now, you've touched on something very close to me. The fact is, for several months now I've been hoping for someone with an interest along these lines. Have you ever heard of a blood bank, Dr. Drew?"

"Yes, I've read of Dr. Fantus' work in Chicago. Also, the work of Duran Jorda in Spain during the Civil War there. The information on this sort of concept seems to be pretty well scattered, but it appears that the preservation and storage of blood is the big problem."

Scudder leaned forward. "Exactly!" He regarded

the young surgeon for several moments. "Tell me, Dr. Drew, what are your personal goals? What have you set out to do?"

"Goals? To be perfectly truthful, I'm extremely interested in doing whatever I can to bring the Negro doctor into a more prominent position in medicine."

"I see. And this appointment of yours here is a step in that direction? And that's the reason you went to Howard as an instructor rather than going into private practice? A good surgeon can do a lot better financially in private practice than he can instructing in a medical school. For that matter, he can do better instructing in a medical school than he can here on a fellowship. You realize, of course, that your salary for the next two years will be about on a par with that of a street sweeper?"

Charlie laughed. "I hadn't thought about it in exactly that way, Dr. Scudder."

Scudder was sizing his man up, and now he shook his head. "I'm sure you hadn't. Now, then, about your field of research. A committee here at Presbyterian Hospital is taking into consideration the possibility of establishing a blood bank. Up to the present time, blood banks, such as the one Dr. Fantus set up in Cook County Hospital, have been primarily supplied on short notice by friends or relatives of patients who needed transfusions. We've still got the big problems of preservation and storage for longer periods than are now possible."

"The changes in chemical structure with time seems to be the principal problem," Drew said.

"Potassium is released by the red cells," Scudder went on. "The breakdown of the red cells is the area that needs looking into."

"The Russians have done some interesting things with cadaver blood," Drew said.

Scudder could see why Dr. Howes had recommended the young man so highly. This was precisely the sort of person that was needed in research. "Very well, Dr. Drew. You can begin immediately. You'll find virtually everything ever published in the field either here at the Center or in the library downtown at the Academy of Medicine." Scudder stood abruptly and held out his hand. "It's good to have you with us. Work up your program, and we'll go over it together."

Drew set to work at once. Long hours were spent in the libraries at Columbia and at the Academy of Medicine. There was not a great deal of material available on the preservation of blood, but he dug out everything he could find. His flair for organizing brought all this material together, and he went to Dr. Scudder with his program for picking up the research where others had stopped.

Scudder was so impressed with the young surgeon's ability that within a matter of weeks after his arrival Charlie Drew was sharing an office with the research director.

Several mornings a week were spent in surgery,

but these grew less and less as the blood research progressed.

Dr. Scudder spoke with Dr. Whipple about the newcomer one morning in early September. "He's the most brilliant man I've got working with me," Scudder said. "I'd like to get him to spend more time in our blood research. You know the talk that's going around regarding the establishment of an experimental blood bank here at Presbyterian. Drew would be invaluable in such a project. His ability as an organizer is nothing short of remarkable."

"Less surgery and more research, is that it?" mused Whipple. He, too, was greatly impressed with this young doctor from Washington, but he knew the disadvantages of dividing a talented man among too many projects. "All right, John, if Drew agrees."

"I think I can convince him," Scudder said confidently.

He found Charlie half an hour later in the laboratory. Scudder pulled a stool alongside Drew's and told him of the talk with Whipple. "This idea of blood banks is going to be very important," he said. "For one thing, the situation in Europe is growing worse all the time, and when war breaks out, blood is going to be as important as bullets."

Drew replaced a test tube in the rack and nodded. "I know." He turned toward his friend. "Very well, John."

"Good! I'll tell Dr. Whipple, and he'll make the arrangements for less sugery."

More time could now be spent in the laboratory, and though Drew missed the surgery, he became totally engrossed in the research. With a team of pathologists, biologists, chemists, and technicians, Drew conducted countless experiments on the various problems of preservation and storage of blood.

He and Scudder went over the problems and progress almost daily.

"The advantages of storing blood are obvious," Drew said on one such occasion. "Especially in cases of emergency when there mightn't be time to get a donor. But the disadvantages are still there. The blood is older, changes may be taking place that make the blood less desirable for transfusion, or, for that matter, even undesirable. Is this older blood actually dangerous? Is blood kept in a preservative of some kind, sodium citrate, for instance, dangerous after a certain amount of time? And if it is, then what is it in this blood that makes it toxic?"

"You've begun your experiments on this, Charlie. I hope you will have some answers next month."

"Why next month?"

"Because that's when there's to be a meeting to begin exploring the idea of a blood bank."

In his mind Drew was calculating the time. "We're working on the potassium experiments now. I've been studying your papers on potassium poisoning in cases of intestinal obstruction. Can you drop in at the lab about eight tomorrow morning? I'd like to show you what we're up to."

The next morning, Drew explained. "This blood sample here," he said, holding a flask, "has been kept under liquid petroleum as a method of preventing clotting. This"—he picked up another sample—"contains heparin as an anti-clotting agent, and the third sample here contains sodium citrate for the same reason. None of these has prevented the loss of potassium from the cells. Of the three, the citrated blood undergoes the change at a slower rate. However, there seems to be some relation regarding the shape of the container, and we should look into this further. We're also running other experiments using a different percentage of sodium citrate as the anti-clotting agent, but these aren't complete as yet."

The two scientists continued to examine the results, evaluating, discussing.

"There must be an answer, John," Drew said when they were done. "I've been wondering if perhaps we mightn't find it not in whole blood but in some substitute."

"Perhaps, Charlie. But with what we have, I think we've got a convincing case to set the wheels in motion for a trial blood bank here at Presbyterian." Scudder looked up at the wall clock. They had been checking the experiments and going over the data for almost the entire morning. "It's almost noon, Charlie. Let's go down to the cafeteria and grab a bite to eat."

8 At the Frontiers of Science

In order to move forward into the unknown, it was necessary to make a thorough exploration of the past. Drew had been doing this for years, but with nothing like the concentration with which he now attacked the subject. He became a familiar figure in the vast libraries at the Center and the Academy of Medicine. He had already studied William Harvey, the English physician who, in 1628, first published the theory that the blood circulated through the body. Previously, it had been thought that blood flowed back and forth from the heart in a manner similar to the ebb and flow of the ocean tides. Harvey had met the fate reserved for men who venture against the beliefs of the centuries. He was ridiculed by his contemporaries, called "the circulator," and only after many years of perseverance did he begin to carry his point.

One important link eluded Harvey, however, and that was the way in which the circulating blood went from the arteries carrying it from the heart into the veins, which returned it.

This was to be the contribution of Marcello Malpighi, who was born in a valley in the Apennine Mountains, near Bologna, Italy, the same year that William Harvey published his revolutionary findings in England. During his study of medicine, Malpighi, coming upon Harvey's work, was greatly impressed and began to use Harvey's theory in his lectures when he became a teacher in Pisa, although it was forbidden by the authorities. The question of how the blood went from arteries to veins was still the major stumbling block to the circulation theory, even for enlightened men such as Malpighi.

By chance, the Italian doctor heard of an invention in Holland, a thing called a microscope, which was little more than an interesting toy used for magnification of small objects. Malpighi saw another possibility in the instrument, and after years of work studying the respiratory systems of frogs, discovered at last the vital link. A network of tiny tubes appeared beneath the lenses of his microscope, and Malpighi traced the course of blood through these hair-like passages, proving that the blood did, indeed, make a circuit back to the heart. He called them capillaries, after the Italian word for hair.

Thirty-three years had passed since William Harvey's belief was published. Harvey himself was dead, but now his theory was backed up by irrefutable proof. It was no longer a theory. It was a medical fact.

In his reading, Charlie Drew went back into the dim corridors of mythology. He read of Jason, who had implored his sorceress wife to restore youth to Aeson, his aged father, on the occasion of the return to Colchis of the Argonauts.

In the ancient writings he read: "Medea unsheathed her knife and cut the old man's throat, then, letting the old blood run out, she filled the veins with a brew so potent that a withered olive branch with which she stirred it at once bore leaves and fruit. When Aeson had drunk this, in part through his lips and in part through his wound, his beard and his hair lost their hoary gray and quickly became black again; went the pallor and look of neglect; the deep wrinkles were filled out with new flesh; his limbs had the strength of youth, and Aeson was filled with wonder."

The dream was an old one. Of course, there was no returning to youth from old age, but Charlie had seen many times the wondrous effects of administering blood to young and old alike. In many ways, the old feelings of mythology still lingered in people's minds.

Blood was a thing of mystery, bringing with it both fear and wonder.

More often in early times it was not the value of blood in restoring physical properties which made it sought after but its metaphysical attributes. The Greek physician, Galen, taught in the second century A.D. that the blood and the natural spirit arose in the liver, and were carried to the heart where they combined with the vital spirit, and then went on to the brain to be perfected into the animal spirit. These three elements were thought to be necessary for a complete soul, and it was for the purpose of restoring these elements that the blood of young warriors was recommended as a draught.

Charlie's reading brought him on through the centuries. While Christopher Columbus was busy with his explorations to the west, others were busy in Rome with a different sort of pioneering. In a book entitled *The Life and Times of Savonarola,* the young researcher found an account of the first transfusion given in a manner comparable to the methods of modern times.

"The vital powers of the Pope, Innocent VIII, were rapidly sinking. Every means of restoring his exhausted vitality had been tried in vain, when a doctor proposed to attempt a cure by means of a new instrument for the transfusion of blood. Hitherto, this experiment had been tried only on animals; but now the blood of the decrepit pontiff was to be transfused into the veins of a youth, who gave his own in exchange. Thrice, in fact, was the difficult experiment made. It did no good to the Pope; and the three boys, costing the sum of one ducat apiece, lost their lives through the introduction of air into their veins. The doctor fled, and five days later, Innocent VIII expired."

Charlie laid the book aside and walked to the window of his room overlooking the sprawling metropolis of New York. Almost four and a half centuries later, he mused, and transfusions still had fatal results.

There was a knock at the door, and he turned. "Come in."

The door opened, and Dr. Scudder stepped inside. He glanced at the stacks of books on Drew's desk, picking up one. "Mythology, Harvey, Malpighi, Bischoff . . ." He smiled and shook his head. "Nothing like firm underpinnings, Charlie."

"There's no need in repeating what's already been proven." His talk with John Beattie came to mind, and the discoveries of Karl Landsteiner. "When you know what's been done, you can try to go on from there."

"It's Friday," Scudder remarked. "You've been putting in about eighteen hours a day, to my knowledge. I want you to take the weekend off."

"But I've got all this!" Drew protested, waving one hand at the books. "And some of the experiments——"

"Forget the books. And make arrangements about the lab work. I want you to come out and spend the weekend with us on Long Island. It might surprise even you what a couple of days of just loafing will do."

"Just loafing" was something Charlie Drew had never done. "Thank you, John. I'd like that very much."

The summer of 1938 passed. In New York's Central Park the leaves fluttered down from the trees. Across the Atlantic Ocean, on September 30, the Prime Minister of England, Neville Chamberlain, returned from Munich and proudly waved a paper as he alighted from his airplane at London Airport. It was a signed pact with Adolf Hitler, in which Germany had been ceded the Sudetanland. Chamberlain fully believed that this act meant "peace in our time." Its real meaning, however, was that Hitler now knew Britain and France would back down rather than risk a war, and so the world continued to move on toward the holocaust that would soon engulf it.

Of more direct importance to Charles Drew at the time was the work of a doctor in Spain. In a medical journal, he read of the continuing work of Dr. Duran Jorda who, in 1936, had organized for the Republican Army of Spain the best system of collection and distribution of blood up until that time. Under the name of the Barcelona Blood Transfusion Service, Jorda had access to some 29,000 donors. He designed a hermetically sealed container in which he stored typed blood, using a glucose citrate mixture to prevent clotting. The blood was delivered to the battlefields in refrigerated trucks and railway cars, and Jorda distributed almost 9,000 liters of this blood before General Franco's forces won the civil war. Working with Jorda had been an old friend of Charlie's from McGill, a surgery instructor, Dr. Norman Bethune. Drew recalled that it had been Bethune who gave John Beattie the article about the Russian experiments using cadaver blood.

Closer to home, the man Charlie had mentioned in his first interview with Scudder, Dr. Bernard Fantus, had established a central depot at Cook County Hospital in Chicago, where blood donors were sent to have blood drawn and stored for future use. Dr. Fantus called his system a "blood bank," thus originating the term. The name was not simply a metaphor, as he pointed out in his report.

"Just as one cannot draw money from a bank unless one has deposited some, so the blood preservation department cannot supply blood unless as much comes in as goes out."

This was the thing that caught Drew's fancy—the blood bank.

In the autumn of 1938, the few blood banks that existed were able to keep blood for days and, in some cases, a week or more. What, exactly, were the changes that took place in blood between the time it was taken from one human being and the time it was reintroduced into the bloodstream of another?

The makeup of blood was carefully analyzed. It was fifty-five percent plasma, a watery, straw-colored liquid, which in turn consisted of hundreds of different chemical compounds, one of which was fibrinogen, the principal protein that caused the clotting of blood.

Without it, a tiny cut could cause a man to bleed to death. The remaining forty-five percent was made up of blood cells, almost all of which were the red cells, or, more scientifically, *erythrocytes.* There were also the disease-fighting white cells, or *leucocytes.* Like all the tissues of the living body, each component had its specific tasks to carry out. The five quarts of blood circulating in the average person distributed oxygen and food and carried wastes away to the organs whose task it was to remove them from the body.

Drew began his studies with the most obvious change in preserved blood, *hemolysis,* or the breaking down of the red cells. It was known that the element potassium was released during this process, causing a toxic effect if the blood was then used for transfusion.

In the laboratory, Charlie worked on his experiments. With the team of highly skilled biologists, pathologists, and chemists, the effects of various chemicals used to keep the blood from clotting were tested. Under the microscope, the changes in cell structure were studied. The results after a day, a week, and longer were recorded. It was found that the red cells became more and more fragile with age, and hence, more susceptible to hemolysis. After less than two weeks, blood preserved in sodium citrate began to show signs of hemolysis.

The breakdown of the red cells, it was found, could be slowed by refrigeration, as well as by careful handling of the blood after it had been drawn from the donor.

More and more experiments were carried out, each adding another brick to the structure of knowledge. Drew and John Scudder continued to talk of the possibility of an experimental blood bank at Presbyterian Hospital.

"It would serve two purposes," Drew said. "First, provide blood quickly for hospital patients and, secondly, give us firsthand information on the use of stored blood."

"Continue your experiments," Scudder said. "The more information we come up with, Charlie, the more likely we are to get the necessary funds to start the blood bank."

The laboratory work went on unceasingly. Drew also participated in clinical studies and was a familiar figure in the wards, taking blood samples and running tests. He kept careful records on all transfusions done at the hospital. In the majority of cases there was no reaction, but in some there would be a rise in temperature, in others a chill. Still other patients would break out in a rash, or develop jaundice. There seemed to be a definite relationship with the age of the blood used.

In some cases, blood plasma—blood with the cells removed—was used, and in his notes Charlie Drew wrote during the winter of 1939: "The experience of the clinic is limited at the present in the use of plasma transfusions. The few tried have worked well, and there have been no reactions."

The ominous clouds of war were on his mind. Men wounded on the battlefronts would desperately need fresh blood or a blood substitute able to sustain circulation in the critical hours following their injury. Plasma, because it could be stored for lengthy periods without substantial changes in its properties, might well hold the key. It certainly justified further investigation.

One day in late winter, Dr. John Scudder came into the laboratory where Drew was working over a rack of test tubes. "Charlie, I'd like you to go to lunch with me today, down at Rockefeller Institute. There's someone I think you should meet. Can you be ready at noon?"

Drew looked up from his work and assented. "Your office at noon."

The two scientists talked of the progress of the work as they drove to the Institute. Scudder had not said who it was they were to meet, and Drew assumed it would be a routine matter. They entered the dining room, and Scudder glanced around until he recognized his man alone at a table near the windows. He hustled his colleague across the room.

"Come along, Charlie. Mustn't keep him waiting."

The tall, white-haired man rose as they approached. John Scudder shook hands with him, then said, "Charlie, I'd like you to meet Dr. Karl Landsteiner. Dr. Landsteiner, this is Dr. Charles Drew."

The two men shook hands. As Charlie felt the firm grip, he was filled with delight. Karl Landsteiner! The man was far more a legend than a flesh and blood human. It was like shaking the hand of William Harvey or Pasteur, someone out of the historical past. Actually, the discoveries that had brought Landsteiner the Nobel prize had been made before Drew was born. He recalled the day, years before at McGill, when John Beattie had told him of the prize being awarded Landsteiner.

"It's an honor, sir," Charlie said with all sincerity.

There was little small talk during the meal. Scudder and Drew told of the blood preservation experiments going on at Presbyterian. As the young Negro spoke of his work, Landsteiner's eyes twinkled. He recognized the signs, the spirit and challenge of the born researcher. Later, Landsteiner told them of the work he was engaged in. "Dr. Alexander Werner and I are working on something new which we call the Rh factor. This is a substance we have found to be present in the red cells of most individuals, and when this combines with certain proteins in the blood, the red cells will clump. As you know, clumping of the red cells may cause serious illness, even death. The Rh factor is inherited, and we now believe it may be the cause of serious brain damage, severe anemia, and death in newborn children. By tests made on the mother's blood during pregnancy, we hope to be able to treat this medically, perhaps by completely replacing the infant's blood with fresh blood shortly after birth."

As they parted, Landsteiner spoke of a need for more blood, and Drew promised to send all he could. "Presently, we're discarding samples after they become a week old. If these will do, I'll have them sent to you."

"It would be a great help, Dr. Drew," Landsteiner answered.

Charlie kept his promise, and thus had an indirect part in the discovery of the Rh system so vitally important to both mothers and those receiving blood transfusions today.

9 Striving Upward: *Banked Blood*

Charles Drew was beginning to make a name for himself. Back in Washington, at Howard Medical School, his friends and colleagues heard of the work he was doing in blood research. The confidence that Dr. Howes and Dean Adams had shown in Drew was being backed up a hundred percent by the young surgeon's performance.

One afternoon in late March of 1939, Drew found a letter waiting when he got back to his quarters after finishing a lengthy experiment in the laboratory. The return address was Howard University, and Charlie opened it and lay down on his bed to read.

"Dear Dr. Drew:

I'm sure you're familiar with the John T. Andrews Memorial Clinic held each year at Tuskegee Institute, in Tuskegee, Alabama. Some of us from Howard go down each year for the seminars and conferences, and we'd like very much to have you come along this year and make a talk on blood transfusions. I sincerely hope that you will be able to take time off from your busy schedule there to make the trip.

The conferences begin on April 6th, and you should plan for a week off, if possible." The letter was signed, "Numa P.G. Adams, Dean."

Drew sighed and put the letter down. Dean Adams was right about the busy schedule. Still, this was an opportunity to bring some of the findings of basic research before practicing physicians—and Negro physicians, at that. It could be a small link in bridging the gap that existed between the fields of research and the clinical application of those findings. Again, he thought of Karl Landsteiner's discovery of blood groups as long ago as 1900, and almost forty years later they were still little known to many doctors. The focus brought to bear on Landsteiner by the Nobel prize had helped, but even that had not done the job entirely.

Drew clasped his hands behind his head, and a slow smile crept over his features. It would be good to see the old crowd from Howard.

On April 2, Drew boarded a Washington-bound train at Grand Central Station. Dr. Scudder had been very pleased at the invitation for Charlie to speak at

Tuskegee and had agreed without hesitation to the time off. Drew worked on his talk during the 225-mile train ride, making certain all the important factors of blood transfusions were included, as well as some of the still experimental areas that he was entering into in his laboratory work.

After spending a day with his family in Washington, Charlie joined his fellow doctors for the drive to Alabama. They planned a one-night stop with friends in Atlanta, and it was just at dusk that they pulled up before a two-story brick house near the Spelman College campus on Atlanta's west side.

Tired and hungry, the group was delighted to find the dinner table set. There were flowers and candlelight and charming company. To Charlie Drew, long accustomed to the plain fare of the hospital, this was truly a banquet.

Among the young teachers who entertained them was one who immediately caught Charlie's eye. She was a tall, pretty Home Economics teacher from Philadelphia. Lenore Robbins was her name, and after dinner she and Charlie took a leisurely walk in the garden.

The following morning, as the group of doctors drove on to Tuskegee, Drew found that his mind was in a virtual fog. Try as he would to keep up with the conversation, he found his thoughts wandering back to Atlanta and the beautiful young teacher from Philadelphia. He was now almost thirty-five years old, and while he had known a great many girls in high school, college, and afterward and had been quite fond of more than one of them, he had never been struck like this before.

The meetings at Tuskegee went well, with Drew's talk on blood transfusion one of the highlights. A few days later, as the conference came to a close, Drew approached Dean Adams.

"I've decided to go back by train," he said. "I'll be leaving tonight so that I can make a stop in Atlanta. I've . . . I've got something very important to attend to before going on to New York."

"If you like, Charlie. Will we see you in Washington, or are you going directly to New York?"

"I think I'd better get back, sir. I've some plans I want to talk over with Dr. Whipple, and the sooner the better."

It was well past midnight when Dr. Charles Drew looked out the window of the grimy coach reserved for Negroes and saw the lights of the Georgia capital. The local train was to make up in Atlanta with the New York Limited, and there was a two-hour layover before the train started the journey northward.

Charlie climbed the steps of Union Station, found a cab, and gave the driver an address. Fifteen minutes later the taxi pulled to the curb before the house where Lenore Robbins and a number of other young women who taught at Spelman lived. The windows were dark, and only a single night light on the porch glowed.

"Wait for me," Charlie said to the driver as he got

out. He rang the doorbell, and when no one answered, he began to knock loudly. A light came on, and moments later the door opened a crack to reveal the headmistress.

"I'm Dr. Drew," he explained quickly to allay her fears. "I'd like to see Miss Robbins."

"Dr. *Drew!* Do you know what time it is? It's long past midnight! Our rules——"

He interrupted gently but firmly. "Yes, I know. But my train leaves shortly for New York, and I barely have time to ask Lenore to marry me."

Dr. Charles Drew was completely oblivious to the dirt and discomfort of the railway coach that carried him northward that night and the following day. Lenore Robbins had accepted his proposal of marriage, and his mind was filled with the future. They had set the date tentatively for the following fall.

Back at the medical center, Dr. John Scudder, as well as Drew's many other friends and co-workers, was delighted with the news.

"The thing I don't understand, Charlie," Scudder remarked good-humoredly, "is how you managed to elude marriage for thirty-five years."

"Maybe I've been too single-minded," Drew quipped. "But I'm glad I waited. You'll understand when you meet her."

Charles Drew had now been at Columbia-Presbyterian for almost a year, and he had definite ideas about the months remaining on his fellowship. He discussed his feelings with John Scudder.

"I'd like to try for the Doctor of Science in Medicine degree," he said. "My thesis would be the original blood studies we're doing."

Scudder answered, "It'd be quite an accomplishment, Charlie. You'll have to talk to Dr. Whipple about it, get his permission."

This would most definitely be, as Scudder said, quite an accomplishment. No Negro physician in the country had yet earned this advanced degree, although attempts had been made. Charlie Drew saw it not as a personal goal but as a step forward for the Negro in medicine—another hurdle taken, and made less difficult for those to follow.

There would be opposition, just as there always had been. But he had been assured of John Scudder's backing, and Drew made an appointment with Dr. Whipple the following week.

There was another subject Charlie planned to bring up at the meeting, and that was the possibility of his taking the examination for the American Board of Surgery as soon as he was eligible, which would be during the coming summer. He also wanted to get back to surgery after so many months of laboratory work and study.

At the appointed time, Drew sat in Dr. Whipple's office and discussed his ideas. Whipple was very pleased with the young surgeon's desire to work toward a higher degree.

"The work you and John Scudder have been doing in blood is very promising, Dr. Drew," said the older man. "I think this research will prove to be of great value in the years to come."

Drew emerged from the meeting with a smiling face. "Everything's set," he told Scudder. "I'm registered for the degree, and Dr. Whipple is going to back me in taking the examinations this summer."

"Wonderful, Charlie. And by the way, the blood bank has been approved. We're to set up an experimental unit this summer, to run on a trial basis for four months."

Everything seemed to be falling into place. Charlie Drew was assigned the task of drawing up the actual blueprint for the blood bank. Several weeks later, when the groundwork for the unit had been laid, space was made available in the splint room on the fourteenth floor of the hospital. Money was appropriated for the project, and work was begun. A staff was picked, with Charlie Drew as its chief. The bank was to operate on an experimental basis for four months, its objectives to ascertain the safest methods of preserving blood for transfusion purposes, as well as to study the physical, chemical, and biological changes that take place during the storage of blood kept in various types of containers, with different methods of preventing clotting.

In August, the blood bank was ready to operate. The head nurse of the project, Miss Helen Stoddard, had worked closely with Drew through all the details of preparation. Now it was done.

In the gleaming workroom of the bank, she sat down wearily. "All we need now, Dr. Drew, is blood."

Charlie began to roll up his sleeve. "Get the equipment ready, Miss Stoddard. I'm your first customer."

Others on the staff volunteered, and by evening a row of bottles, containing typed, citrated blood, stood on the shelves of the bank's vault—a refrigerator.

At its start, the blood bank was not meant to be a full functioning part of the hospital service. Cases were to be selective so that studies of them could be kept accurate and complete. The bank was to be available in emergencies, of course, but these were kept to a minimum, with Drew having the prerogative of selecting cases.

Any ward of the hospital requesting blood from the bank could do so only by going into "debt" for the amount drawn and making up this amount or by previously having made a "deposit" in the bank. The operation was relatively simple, and detailed records were kept on each case.

Virtually all fatalities resulting from blood transfusions were known to come from mistakes in the grouping or cross-matching of blood types. Great care was taken in this. A finger-tip sample was taken from each donor before the blood was drawn, and also a sample of the blood drawn was sent to the laboratory separately to have the groupings double-checked. A patient requiring blood from the bank was similarly checked to avoid error.

The blood bank went well from the start, and it

appeared that when the four-month trial period ended there would be an extension. Additional funds were made available for the operation of the bank, and this most helpfully avoided the possibility of having to cut down on the already small staff.

As summer's end drew near and his wedding date was only weeks away, Charlie Drew added to his small income by allowing himself to be used as a human "guinea pig" in another of the Center's experimental programs.

On September 23, 1939, Charlie took a train to Philadelphia, where he and Lenore Robbins were married. The newlyweds returned to New York, to a modest apartment Charlie had found at not too great a distance from the Medical Center. Commuting by subway, his day began at eight o'clock as a member of a surgical team. This occupied the morning, and after a quick lunch in the cafeteria, his afternoons were spent in the laboratory carrying on his blood experiments, gathering and organizing material for his doctoral thesis on banked blood. When this was finished, there was work to be done in the blood bank itself, and it was often late when Charlie arrived home.

The four-month trial period of the blood bank came to an end in November, and as had been anticipated, the results were so promising that the bank was made a permanent service of Presbyterian Hospital.

Meanwhile, with the data already gathered and the experiments running continuously, Drew began to lean more toward the use of blood plasma as a substitute for whole blood. The concept was not new, but it had never before gained much support, and there was much to be learned about it. In actual clinical use, even with limited knowledge, blood plasma seemed to bring about none of the reactions that still occurred in the use of whole blood.

In the early winter of 1939–40 he talked often with Scudder about increasing their investigation into plasma. "It contains everything but the blood cells," Charlie pointed out, "and the chemical breakdown of the red cells seems to be one of our biggest stumbling blocks in prolonged storage of blood."

Scudder agreed that more work needed to be done. Over the years, beginning about 1920, there had been scattered experimentation. Now, as has so often been the case throughout history, the looming threat of war was a spur to scientific advancement. In January of 1940, the Blood Transfusion Association made funds available to Presbyterian Hospital for the purpose of carrying out laboratory and clinical studies relating to the preservation of plasma and its use as a blood substitute.

Drew was elated. He felt deeply that the answer to a great many problems lay in this direction. In addition to its stability, plasma had another advantage. As the blood cells of whole blood were not present, there was no necessity for typing of plasma. This would be especially valuable under the conditions of battle.

The research was to be carried out over a six-month period into the following June, which would coincide with the end of Charlie's two-year fellowship.

Meantime, the pages of Charlie's doctoral thesis, *Banked Blood,* continued to mount. He read hundreds of books and papers, many of which he had to have translated from other languages. The data from his experiments began to take shape. His oral examination was to be taken in January and the thesis submitted in the spring. The oral examination was passed with flying colors. The examiners were greatly impressed by Drew's depth of knowledge of his subject.

Then he began to give shape to his thesis. He broke it into four principle sections. First was the evolution of the blood bank; second, the known changes in preserved blood; third, his own experimental studies in blood preservation; and finally, the organization, operation, and success of the blood bank at Presbyterian Hospital.

The decision that winter to delve into the possibilities of blood plasma had come too late for this to be a major part of Drew's thesis, as his work on it was nearing completion by that time. He spent many hours each day in plasma experiments, while at the same time continuing his other work. He carried a staggering work load, one that would have defeated a lesser man.

There was very little time off. Occasionally, perhaps, there would be a movie, but he preferred entertainment to "message" films. Another interest that stayed with Charlie Drew was sports. He particularly liked to see a professional football game. Whenever he, or one of the other doctors, could get tickets to a New York Giants game, Charlie would do everything he could to rearrange his schedule to include it.

The winter of 1939–40 passed. The days grew warmer. At last, the thesis was finished and submitted to the examining board. In the words of Drew's friend and mentor, Dr. John Scudder, it was a "monumental work." It brought into sharp focus everything that had gone before and combined it with the original work done at Columbia-Presbyterian Medical Center over the nearly two years Charlie Drew had been there. It was a very real guide to the founding of other blood banks, and in the near future would play a key role in the good not only of Americans but of people all over a war-torn world.

10 Time of Crisis

On a morning in the late spring of 1940, a technician came into the laboratory where Charlie Drew was conducting plasma experiments. "Dr. Scudder would like you to come to his office, Dr. Drew."

Drew nodded, jotted the experiment observations in a notebook, and went down the corridor to the research director's office.

"An emergency meeting's been called by the Blood Transfusion Association, Charlie," Scudder said. "They want us there to present the case for plasma." Scudder glanced at his watch. "Barely time to take off your smock and grab your coat. Are we ready?"

Charlie laughed. "I think so."

The meeting was top level. Dr. Alexis Carrel, who in 1912 had won a Nobel prize for his work in blood-vessel surgery and the transplant of organs and tissues, was present. Carrel had just returned from France. Also at the conference table was another Nobel prize winner, Karl Landsteiner. Seated alongside Carrel was an officer wearing the uniform of the French Air Force and beyond him Dr. Max Strumia, Dr. E.H.L. Corwin, an officer of the U.S. Army, as well as experts from the Rockefeller Institute, National Research Council, the Academy of Medicine, and representatives from several large pharmaceutical firms.

The meeting was begun without delay, Dr. Carrel speaking first. Small, white-haired, neatly dressed, he rose and looked around the table. "The situation in Europe, as you're all aware, is grave. There is, of course, no way of knowing how widespread this war will become, but the need for blood is already acute in France and will become much more so in the very near future. I am here, along with Colonel Aumont of the French Air Force, to appeal for your help. Your experience in the field of blood banks over the past months can be of invaluable aid. France needs our help now."

A doctor at the far end of the table made a suggestion. "Could we send medical teams to draw blood from civilian and military donors in France? This sort of thing was successful in Spain, as you know, under the direction of Dr. Duran Jorda."

The French colonel answered. "This is being done

at the present time, and it will undoubtedly save many lives. But it is simply not enough."

"There is the problem of time," Carrel said. "Under ideal conditions, stored whole blood begins to deteriorate in a relatively short time. Under the conditions that now prevail in France . . ." He shrugged. "The work that you gentlemen have been doing in the field of plasma may provide our answer."

John Bush, the president of the Blood Transfusion Association, rose to his feet. "Dr. Scudder and Dr. Drew have been carrying out experiments under an Association grant since last January at Presbyterian Hospital."

All eyes turned toward the two men. "Charlie," Scudder said quietly, "tell them about it."

Charles Drew stood. He looked around at his impressive audience and began to speak, telling in detail of the experiments in the preparation, preservation, and use of plasma. "Our scale to date has necessarily been small, but the conclusions we've reached are most promising. Plasma, being whole blood with the cells removed, bridges one problem, and that is the necessity for the typing of blood before performing a transfusion. Also, under very strict sanitary conditions in its preparation, a plasma-saline solution is far more stable during long periods of storage than is whole blood. Actually, dried plasma would be preferable, but as yet our techniques have not been perfected. Therefore, it is a liquid plasma solution that we propose. In the great majority of cases—burns, shock, loss of blood—it has proven to be a highly effective substitute for whole blood."

Not all present were entirely convinced. "You admit yourself, Dr. Drew, that your work in plasma is still virtually in the experimental stage," said one of the doctors. "Perhaps we could fly whole blood to France for the present, thus cutting down the time between the drawing and use of the blood, while at the same time continuing the plasma experiments."

Dr. Karl Landsteiner took the floor. The man, whose discovery of blood groups had been the key to successful blood transfusions, now spoke on behalf of plasma, which bypassed the need for grouping.

"It is true, as Dr. Drew has said, that plasma is yet in the experimental stage, but let us not overlook the fact, gentlemen, that we are not living in a time of peace. Let the experiments continue, of course. But under the emergency conditions that exist today in Europe, we have enough knowledge to justify an effort at quantity production of plasma to treat the casualties of war."

With Landsteiner backing him, Charlie Drew continued. "If we attempt to ship whole blood, the chances are we will see a very high percentage of a useless product arrive where it is urgently needed. Liquid plasma has a far longer shelf life than whole blood, and our losses due to spoilage or contamination would be greatly reduced."

The discussion went on for some time, and in the end it was agreed that a "Plasma for France" project would be begun. Drs. Drew, Scudder, and Corwin were appointed as a committee to recommend what personnel, equipment, and procedures would be needed and to enlist the aid of various hospitals in the New York area.

As the meeting was adjourned and Drew gathered his papers, John Scudder said, "You know, Charlie, there's one problem facing us that wasn't brought up today. On a large scale, what will be the reaction of the public to requests for the donation of blood to be given to strangers thousands of miles away?"

"I've wondered about that," Drew replied. "In our blood bank it's generally friends or relatives of the patient who donate. But in something as big and new as this, well, we'll have to wait and see."

The work of the committee was a full-time job in itself. Charlie Drew shouldered his share of it, while keeping up with his other work as well. Virtually unnoticed in those hectic days was an event that took place on Tuesday, June first, just three days before Charlie Drew's thirty-sixth birthday. Based on his 245-page thesis, *Banked Blood,* his oral examinations, and other requirements, the degree of Doctor of Science in Medicine was conferred upon him by Columbia University, making him the first Negro doctor to attain this degree.

His work in New York was now almost done. With the advanced degree and the things he had learned during the course of his fellowship, he was ready to go back to Howard and put his knowledge to good use. He saw in his future there something he considered of paramount importance—the training of Negro doctors.

A few weeks later the special committee completed its work and submitted the report to the Blood Transfusion Association. The project for blood for France was about to get under way.

In the meantime, the war machine of the German Third Reich moved swiftly and invincibly through the spring and early summer of 1940. The Nazi legions crossed the borders of France, flanked the outmoded Maginot Line, and by June 14 the storm troopers were marching into Paris. A week later an armistice was signed with Adolf Hitler by the Vichy government of France.

Because the fall of France took place with such awesome suddenness, the plasma project lost headway. His work in New York done, Charlie Drew, his wife, and their infant daughter bade farewell to their friends and went back to Washington, where he had received an appointment as assistant professor in the Department of Surgery at Howard Medical School. They moved into a faculty house on campus only a block from the school and Freedman's Hospital. This was, as Drew had said, his "next big meet."

But the events of history were not to allow him to remain for long. In Europe, the Nazi hordes had hammered the stunned British Expeditionary Force back to the Straits of Dover, and between May 26 and June 4, the heroic evacuation of thousands of soldiers took place on the beaches of Dunkirk while under constant German bombardment and attack.

The British pulled back onto their islands, fully expecting invasion to follow. But the expected did not happen. Instead of shiploads of Nazi soldiers, there came planeloads of bombs. In late summer, the blitz began. Squadrons of bombers, with the swastika on their wings, roared across the English Channel from the continent, striking indiscriminately and viciously at cities all over the British Isles. The raiders came by the hundreds, night and day. The hard-pressed fighters of the Royal Air Force battled valiantly. The Spitfires took their toll, but they were unable to stop the *Luftwaffe* entirely, and city after city found itself in flaming ruins when the all-clear was sounded.

In the ruins were people—thousands of them—dead, dying, or wounded. Scores of hospitals so desperately needed in those dark hours were themselves flattened masses of rubble. People whose lives might otherwise have been saved now died for lack of adequate medical treatment. There were not enough doctors, not enough hospital beds, nurses, or drugs. Very high on the list of needs was blood.

With the groundwork already laid for its initial proposal to help France, the Blood Transfusion Association in New York offered its help. Six large metropolitan hospitals had already agreed to join the program. The British gratefully accepted the offer, and in August a program unlike any before in history was begun.

Each hospital, working independently, began the

collection of blood and the processing of plasma, using the techniques perfected by Drew the previous winter and spring. Almost at once, problems arose. One of the shipments of preserved plasma, more than two hundred liters, went to the bottom of the Atlantic off the coast of Ireland with the torpedoing of the S.S. *Western Prince*. Losses such as this were expected, even inevitable. But other losses were of a different nature. Whether sent by ship or by plane, an alarming amount of the desperately needed plasma was found to be contaminated on arrival in Britain, totally unfit for use. Also, some of the participating hospitals in New York failed to meet their quotas due to a lack of blood donors. Standards were not uniform, and the program, so brilliantly conceived, seemed on the verge of failure.

There was deep concern among those involved on both sides of the Atlantic. In England, an old friend of Charlie Drew's, Dr. John Beattie, was head of the Royal Air Force Transfusion Service and in daily contact with the problems of the program. He and Drew had kept in touch over the years, and Beattie felt his old friend might be the help they needed.

At a meeting in London the situation of the blood program was discussed. Beattie addressed the group of officers and doctors.

"The fact that some of the plasma is entirely free from contamination proves that the program can be successful. Tighter controls, and a more uniform method of collecting, processing, and shipping are needed."

"But we've reported to the American authorities on each shipment," said a gray-haired major. "What more can we do at this end?"

Beattie clasped his hands behind his back and paced to the window. The sun was obliterated not by the London fog but by the heavy pall of smoke that hung over the city. "I've an idea. Organization, quick and sure, is what is called for. Dr. Charles Drew, one of the men who led the research into plasma during the past year, was a student and close friend of mine while I was at McGill Medical School. I believe he might be the man who could get us on an even keel."

"Drew?" mused one of the doctors. "But he's with the program now, isn't he?"

Beattie shook his head. "He's in Washington, teaching surgery at Howard Medical School. He's young, a brilliant researcher, but not one of your laboratory recluses. And"—he looked around at the group—"he's a Negro."

"You say that in a rather gloomy tone, Beattie," said the major.

Beattie smiled. "The Americans are not directly involved with the war . . . yet. But they have their problems."

"Then what you are suggesting might make matters worse instead of better," said a representative of the Royal Navy. "Why specify this Dr. Drew for the

American blood program? Why not try to find someone who might be more—more acceptable over there?"

"For the simplest reason I can think of, sir," Beattie replied. "In my estimation, Charlie Drew is beyond a doubt the best qualified man in the entire world."

Outside the building an all too familiar wailing sound split the air, the sound of the air raid siren. Beattie slowly gathered up his papers. "And now, gentlemen," he said calmly, "it seems as though Jerry is about to pay us another call. Shall we adjourn to the bomb shelter?"

The following day a cablegram went out from the Air Ministry in London to the Blood Transfusion Association in New York. It was signed by Dr. John Beattie, and it read:

Uniform standards for all blood banks of utmost importance. Suggest you appoint overall director if program is to continue. Suggest Dr. Charles R. Drew if available.

A second cablegram went directly to Drew at Howard University:

Could you secure five thousand ampoules dried plasma for transfusion work immediately and follow this by equal quantity in three to four weeks. Contents each ampoule should represent about one pint whole plasma.

John Beattie
Chief Transfusion Service, RAF

In his small office at Howard, Drew read the cablegram with curiosity. In the first place, it was doubtful that that amount of dried plasma was in existence, and, secondly, he was puzzled by the direct request from Beattie who knew he was no longer working in New York.

Later, at home, Drew received a telegram from the Blood Transfusion Association, which quickly cleared up the second point. He was needed in New York immediately, and a leave of absence for their new assistant professor was being requested of the Howard authorities.

11 Blood for Britain

The Drews had been in their new home in Washington only a few weeks, scarcely time to become settled. Charlie was already enthusiastically putting all his effort into his work. Then came Beattie's plea from England, and close on its heels, the telegram from John Bush, of the Blood Transfusion Association.

It read:

The Board . . . has decided to create a position of full-time medical Supervisor to act as liaison officer between the board and the hospitals engaged in procuring plasma for shipment to the British Red Cross. I am requested to offer this position and all it involves to you as being the best qualified of anyone we know to act in this important development. I am sure your University will feel, under the wartime circumstances, that it should grant you a leave of absence at least until the first of the year to help us in . . . establishing this vital medical relief. Will you please wire or telephone me if you can arrange the matter and in so doing just how long you can remain. . . . I cannot tell you how much depends upon your University and yourself giving us a favorable reply. I await your answer with utmost interest.

Lenore Drew watched in silence as her husband read and reread the telegram. Deep in thought, he suddenly seemed aware that she was standing there.

"Lenore," he said with his familiar grin, "did I give you fair warning as to what you might be getting into when I asked you to marry me?"

"I'm happy, Charlie." She smiled. "No complaints."

"They want me back in New York." He read the wire aloud, then folded it and slipped it into his pocket. "I can't very well turn it down."

"And I'd be the last person who would want you to turn it down! Imagine what it means, being able to put your own research to such important use! You call New York. I'll start packing your things."

Because of their infant daughter, Bebe—whose name was derived from the initials of Blood Bank—it was decided Lenore should remain in Washington. The University authorities unhesitatingly granted Charlie a leave of absence for as long as he might be needed, and the following morning he boarded a train for New York.

He was met at Grand Central Station by John Bush and Dr. John Scudder and whisked at once to Presbyterian Hospital, where a meeting was scheduled. Most of the top people of the program were present—Tracy Vorhees, Dr. DeWitt Stetten, Dr. C.P. Rhoads, and a number of other medical and administrative personnel.

"Being the first project of its kind," John Bush said, "there is neither literature nor past experience on some of the problems we face. Our dominant problem is bacterial contamination of the plasma. Another is lack of uniform procedures in collecting blood and processing the plasma. In order to begin the project without delay, it was agreed to allow each participating hospital to use what equipment it had available at the time, and this has resulted in a wide variation of techniques. A third problem is the failure of several of the hospitals to meet their quotas because of lack of donors, while other hospitals have at times not been able to handle the donors they had available."

Charlie Drew took notes and asked questions as the long meeting progressed into the night. It was unanimously agreed that a central depot was absolutely essential, where all incoming calls from donors could be handled, and where the donors could be assigned to one of the hospitals. All records would be kept here as well.

The New York Academy of Medicine supplied space in its buildings on East 104th Street for this purpose. The telephone company donated a switchboard to handle the calls. An appeal program was planned to include radio, newspapers, subway cards, and other media. Within a week, nine operators waited at the switchboard as the first radio appeal went on the air. Drew, Scudder, John Bush, and a dozen others who had worked unceasingly on the new setup stood by anxiously, watching the switchboard and listening to the radio message. The announcer concluded by giving the number donors could call—Sacramento 2-8590.

Drew turned to Scudder. "Well, John, shall we cross our fingers?"

"Perhaps we should," Scudder agreed.

At that moment, the switchboard became a blaze of lights. The nine operators were swamped with calls. Following the carefully worked-out plan, each caller was assigned to a certain hospital at a given hour to have the blood drawn. The blood of Her Highness the Ranee of Sarawak proved to be no bluer than that of eight hundred WPA workers who volunteered.

With the donor problem solved, other difficulties could now be met. The high ratio of bacteriological contamination of the plasma came under close scrutiny. It was obvious to Drew and his associates that the more important steps in the processing would have to be carried out by a relatively few, well-trained individuals and that the precautions to insure sterility would have to be far more stringent than those required by the

Federal regulations which were followed in the earlier part of the program.

Drew enlisted Dr. Frank Meleney, head of Presbyterian Hospital's Bacteriology Laboratory in this effort. A final laboratory test was made by Meleney and his assistants of all plasma prior to shipment.

Procedures were standardized at all participating hospitals, which by this time totaled nine. Even so, the mass production of human biologicals proved to be vastly more subject to error than small laboratory experiments with the same materials. Losses from contamination continued, but gradually the ratio began to drop.

A report in late fall from the British Transfusion Service had a heartening tone. Detailed accounts of the contamination of earlier shipments were noted, and then reference was made to the second period of the operation, the shipments made after the appointment of Charlie Drew as medical director. This particular period, the report went on to say, had been one of almost total good results. With the exception of two cases of contaminated plasma, all others received had been checked as satisfactory and forwarded to transfusion centers throughout Britain.

The program seemed to be going as well as could be expected. Both purposes of the endeavor—the first, to lend immediate aid to the people of Britain, and the second to gather information that would be of value to the United States should it be pulled into the war—

were being fulfilled. The report from Britain showed that the first goal was being met. As for the second, Drew and everyone else connected with the program were learning more each day.

Public response to appeals for blood donors continued to increase. At the peak of the program there were more than 1,300 donations being made each week at the participating hospitals. The American Red Cross, which had originally joined the Blood Transfusion Association in the project, utilized its publicity department in keeping the need for blood before the public.

Plans were being made for further expansion of the program when, in early November, a letter was received from the authorities in England, stating that they were beginning to operate blood donor centers of their own and that the American aid would be needed only until January or February, at which time the British would be able to supply their own needs.

With this in mind, Drew gradually shifted his efforts away from the project itself and more into experiments investigating the various problems that had come up throughout the program.

One of the principal points that had been raised was that of the relative merits of blood plasma and blood serum, which is plasma with the clotting agent, fibrinogen, removed. In December, Drew, Scudder, and half a dozen other researchers began experiments in this direction, for even with the needs of the British approaching a close, the United States Armed Forces saw the urgent need for the further perfection of a suitable blood substitute.

On January 17, 1941, the final shipment of plasma went out across the Atlantic. The Blood for Britain program was over.

Charlie Drew was given the task of writing the medical report on the program for the Blood Transfusion Association, and with suggestions and editing from other members of the team he had worked with, the full report was published two weeks later.

John Scudder, over coffee at the Academy of Medicine, remarked to his friend, "You were wise to come in September, Charlie. As important as your work at Howard might be, I believe you've made a much greater contribution here."

It was, indeed, wise, and the wisdom of it was not overlooked by others. The Blood Transfusion Association knew the value of the man they had chosen. Columnist Albert Deutsch, not long before, quoted an Association spokesman as saying, "Since Drew, who is a recognized authority on the subject of blood preservation and blood substitutes, and, at the same time, an excellent organizer has been in charge, our major troubles have vanished."

But the need for such a man had not vanished with the end of the Britain program, and if Charlie Drew thought that now he would be returning to his family and his teaching, he was mistaken.

With Great Britain self-sufficient in supplying her own blood needs, the efforts of the Blood Transfusion Association were now applied to a much larger undertaking. A month earlier, Mr. DeWitt Smith, of the American Red Cross, asked the Association to examine the possibilities of a nationwide program which could be quickly carried out for the bleeding of 100,000 donors, the blood to be given to the U.S. Armed Forces.

While the Britain program was tapering off, the Association sought firsthand information from blood banks operating in twelve key cities around the country, ascertaining what facilities were available in each city and which might be used in the coming months for the collection of blood and processing of plasma for the Red Cross purpose.

Charlie Drew, with the success of the Britain project behind, was the logical choice as medical director of the Red Cross program. Howard University had agreed the previous September to extend his leave of absence for as long as necessary, so the decision to stay or to return to Howard was up to Drew himself.

In his office at the Academy of Medicine, he sat down at his desk. For a long moment he gazed out the window at the snow billowing down from the black sky past the light of the window. He was thinking of Lenore and little Bebe and the separation his work necessitated. Was it fair to them? Perhaps, he thought, a man who sets himself such demanding tasks should go it alone.

Outside the open office door there was the sound of footsteps. Dr. Earle Taylor paused at the door and looked in. "Why don't you call it a day, Charlie? It's past ten."

"It has been a long day, Earle," Drew answered. "I'll be leaving soon."

The young doctor glanced toward the window. "Looks as though we might be in for a blizzard. Well, goodnight. See you tomorrow."

The footfalls echoed away, and the deep silence settled about Charlie Drew once more.

Through the silence he seemed to sense the pulse of the great city, of the country itself. Drew, as did many people, felt that the involvement of the United States in the war was inevitable, that only the time remained to be set. His work at Howard would have to wait.

He recalled what John Beattie had spoken of years ago, on a warm spring day in Montreal. Research was the frontier. There were no trails to follow. This was where the pioneers toiled—the Landsteiners, the Harveys, Malphigis.

Of course, there was another frontier—that of the Negro's position in medicine. Perhaps soon he could get back to that. He walked to the window. Snowflakes swirled down from the black sky, and gazing out at the night, he felt a deep loneliness for his family. After a time, he moved to the door, flicked the light off, and walked slowly down the deserted corridor.

Using the facilities and techniques of the Blood for Britain program, the first blood of the American Red Cross project was drawn on February 3, 1941. With Charlie Drew at the helm, the staff consisted of two other doctors—Earle Taylor and Darrell Shaw—four nurses, two technicians, a bookkeeper, secretary, shipping clerk, and handyman. The first week an average of sixty donors a day were bled at the Presbyterian Hospital blood bank.

The next step was the use of mobile units, and in March, Charlie Drew and his team took the first such unit to Farmingdale, Long Island. This proved extremely practical, and the concept was made a basic feature of the national program.

However, an unexpected and disheartening problem arose. The Armed Forces informed the Red Cross that non-Caucasian blood would not be acceptable to them, and from that time on only white donors were used. Thus, a strangely ironical situation was created. Dr. Charles Drew, whose basic research had been one of the most important things in bringing the program into being, and who was now the Medical Director of the Red Cross blood program, could not give his own blood for the cause.

There was no scientific basis for this, as Drew and other informed men knew. It was simply another manifestation of prejudice, and of course it was a source of humiliation to Drew himself. There were also rumors to the effect that when the blood program became a nationwide endeavor Charles Drew might not be the proper man to head it up, even though his record as scientist and administrator was as remarkable as it was unimpeachable.

Never one to avoid an issue, Charlie Drew faced this one squarely. He called his secretary into his office one morning shortly after Negro donors began to be turned away. "Contact the newspapers, please. Set up a news conference for this afternoon if possible, here in my office. I want to make a statement."

At two o'clock a dozen or so reporters were in Drew's office, notebooks in hand. Drew stood behind his desk, his expression somber. "Several of you have made inquiries regarding my opinion of the announced Armed Forces policy of refusing offers of blood from non-Caucasians. I am speaking to you today not as a Negro, but as a scientist and as Director of the Red Cross blood bank program. I will not give you an opinion. I *will* give you the scientific facts in the matter. The blood of individual human beings may differ by blood groupings, but there is absolutely no scientific basis to indicate any difference according to race."

Charlie Drew had made his statement. It was published and backed by various scientific publications, including the "Journal of the American Medical Association." But facts do not generally overcome prejudice. This is done only by the attrition of time, and not many weeks afterward, Dr. Charles Drew submitted his resignation as head of the program.

12 Howard University: New Worlds

Much talent is misdirected and lost in times of great stress, at the precise time such talent is most urgently needed. The ruling of the Armed Forces of the United States stating that Negro blood was not acceptable in the huge blood plasma program just getting under way early in 1941 inevitably cost them the services of the man who was one of the world's top experts on the subject—Dr. Charles Drew.

But the loss to the national blood program was the gain of Howard University's medical school. Drew returned to Washington in April. Changes had taken place at Howard during his absence. Dean Numa

Adams had died, and Dr. Edward Howes, the Chief of Surgery who had been instrumental in securing the Columbia-Presbyterian Fellowship for Drew, had returned to Yale.

But the resident training program at Freedmen's Hospital had got a sound start, and under the successors of both men it continued to move forward. Dr. Joseph L. Johnson, who had become acting dean of the medical college on the death of Dean Adams, welcomed Charlie back to his job as Assistant Professor of Surgery. During the same month, April, Drew was certified as a diplomate of the American Board of Surgery, another significant step for a Negro doctor. By summer's end he was appointed head of the Department of Surgery of the medical school, as well as Chief of Surgery at Freedmen's Hospital. Again, Drew was carrying a staggering work load but showing no apparent strain under it. This was the real work he considered himself cut out for, the training of young Negro surgeons. The accomplishments of the past were, to Drew at least, just that—past.

His students loved him. A Drew lecture was not one to be missed, and at Freedmen's Hospital, across the street from the medical school, word would get around when Dr. Charlie Drew planned to make the rounds of the wards, examining and discussing the cases. Every intern and resident who could possibly manage it would be on hand.

There was no doubt that, had he chosen to do so, Drew could have made in private practice many times the salary he received. But his purpose did not lie in that direction. It was very clear to him what he was doing. In staff meetings he told those who worked with him, "We must stimulate desire in those we teach. A desire not simply to be good surgeons, but to spread themselves around, pass it on, as it were. They must get into the mainstream of surgery and come up to the level of the whites."

His work occupied him almost totally. Even though he lived hardly a block from his small office on the second floor of Freedmen's Hospital, there was little time to putter around the yard or play with Bebe and the newly arrived Charlene. He was much in demand as a speaker, both for scientific and lay groups, and realizing the value of these opportunities, he accepted whenever possible.

One topic Drew spoke on was the relationship of the Negro doctor to the military service. He felt, just as did most medical men—white or black—that winning the war was the prime issue of the moment. But he felt very strongly about the U.S. Army's practice of segregation and even more so about the Navy's policy of excluding Negro doctors from the naval service. It was totally wrong that men who fought in foreign lands in the name of freedom still had not achieved it at home.

He knew the Negro would give a good accounting of himself, and he hoped that this accounting would not go unrecognized when the war was over.

Not yet forty years old himself, Drew weighed the choice of entering the armed forces or staying on at

Howard. He chose the latter as being the place where he could be of most value.

In 1944 he was appointed Chief of Staff of Freedmen's Hospital. The Negro institution, operating at that time under the United States Department of the Interior (later under the Department of Health, Education, and Welfare) was allotted a budget of approximately $1,000,000 a year. This was woefully inadequate, and Charlie Drew set out to do something about it. The procedure in this was to submit a proposed budget to the Interior Department, and from the department it went to a congressional committee for final approval. Drew's first move was to get a list of the names of congressmen on the committee. Because of their usual long tenure of office and the accompanying seniority, many congressmen from southern states were on the committee. Drew then listed the Howard medical students and Freedmen's residents who were from these states. Appearing personally before the committee, he appealed to these southern congressmen on the basis of the money their own states were being saved by the fact that these Negro students could attend Howard and serve their internships and residencies at Freedman's. Drew's efforts over a period of two years resulted in the Freedmen's Hospital budget being increased from $1,000,000 to $3,500,000.

The same year, 1944, a unique honor was bestowed on Drew. He was awarded the Spingarn Medal, which is given annually by the National Association for the Advancement of Colored People. The citation stated that the medal was awarded to Dr. Charles Drew "for his outstanding work in blood plasma. Dr. Drew's research in this field led to the establishment of a blood plasma bank which served as one of the models for the widespread system of blood banks used by the American Red Cross. Dr. Drew was appointed full-time Medical Director for the blood plasma project for Great Britain. The report on this work was published and served as a guide for later developments for the United States Army and for the armies of our Allies."

The award came as a complete surprise to Drew. He had done no work in plasma or blood since leaving the Red Cross program in 1941. Possibly, he thought, the official attitude that had been taken toward Negro blood donors had had some part in his being chosen. The irony that a Negro scientist had been instrumental in the breakthroughs that made the blood program possible might give Negroes everywhere a feeling of satisfaction. The award and its attendant publicity could effectively bring this fact to the attention of the entire country.

There was no doubt that a great deal of bitterness existed not only regarding the blood donor program but about the general treatment and opportunities for Negroes in all facets of the war effort. In honoring one of their own in this manner, perhaps the bitterness would be lessened.

As Chief of Staff at Freedmen's, Charlie Drew once told a friend, "There are two things I'm trying to live down—my football performance and my part in blood plasma work. My job now is in the field of surgery."

The football performance would fade with time. The other would not. When the war was finally over, a battlefield surgeon with the Fifth Army, speaking of the bloody Italian campaign, said that the most important factor in saving so many thousands of American lives was, undoubtedly, the availability of blood plasma. Medical corpsmen at the battlefront were able to administer plasma at the crucial moment, making it possible to evacuate the wounded to field hospitals where surgical miracles were performed, also because fresh blood plasma, flown from Blood Donor Centers in America, was available to the patients.

But Drew was totally committed to the program at Howard and Freedmen's Hospital, and during the late forties very tangible results began to show as the young doctors training under him went on to prove the soundness of his planning.

His enthusiasm was as high as ever when, on the night of March 31, 1950, he attended the Student Council banquet at Howard Medical School. Drew was one of the speakers and at dinner chatted with a friend, Dr. Robert Jason.

"Are you going down to the Tuskegee meetings, Charlie?" Jason asked.

Drew nodded. "I'm driving down with a few of the others. In fact"—he glanced at his watch—"we're leaving as soon as the banquet's over. We can spell each other at the wheel and save time."

"Aren't you going to get some sleep before you go?" Jason asked, concerned.

"We can catch a nap on the way. It's a long drive, and the meetings begin day after tomorrow."

Charlie Drew and three other doctors from Washington left the city at one o'clock on the morning of April 1, stopping every couple of hours to change drivers. At about eight o'clock that morning, Drew was at the wheel. The others were all asleep, and with his thoughts on his work and the steady drone of the engine, for an instant he must have dozed. The wheels caught the shoulder of the road a few miles outside Burlington, North Carolina. His eyes snapped open, he struggled with the wheel, but it was too late. The car spun and flipped over. The three passengers came out with relatively minor injuries. Charlie Drew's chest was crushed against the steering wheel, and despite all efforts to save his life, he died an hour later, barely two months before his forty-sixth birthday.

Where would the determination and talent of Charles Richard Drew have been channeled had he lived? The real beginnings of the great struggle for civil rights lay just ahead. He had long been deeply involved in bettering the lot of his race, and there can be little doubt he would have been in the forefront of the movement.

Drew made an indelible mark in the relatively

brief span of his life. The Negro in medicine today occupies a far better position because of his dedication and persistence. And even the most unbending segregationist whose life might have been saved by a bottle of blood plasma on some distant battlefield owes, in no small measure, his life to a young Negro doctor who worked unceasingly from 1938 to 1941 to overcome the problems of blood plasma preservation.

Charles Drew's death stunned all who knew him or who knew of his work. A glowing tribute was paid him in the Congressional Record.

In the late 1940's, with great accomplishments already behind him, he was looking only to the future. For Drew, his life's story as a physician had just begun.

ampoule. A small, bulbous glass vessel hermetically sealed and used to hold a solution for hypodermic injection.

blood group. One of the four classes into which human beings can be separated on the basis of their possession or nonpossession of certain protein or carbohydrate substances. These substances form the groups *O, A, B, AB*.

embryo. An organism in the early stages of development.

glucose. A sugar present in both plant and animals that is the chief source of protoplasmic energy.

heparin. A substance found in the liver, lungs and other tissues that prolongs the clotting time of blood by preventing the formation of fibrin.

jaundice. A yellowish pigmentation of the skin, tissues and certain body fluids that occurs when bile pigments are deposited in the system due to interference with the natural production and discharge of bile or the excessive breakdown of red blood cells.

obstetrics. A branch of medical science that deals with birth, its antecedents and sequels.

pathology. The study of abnormality; especially the study of diseases, their essential nature, causes and development, and the structural and functional changes caused by them.

pathology (humoral). The study of abnormality in the functioning fluids or semifluids of the body, such as blood, lymph or bile.

pediatrics. A branch of medicine that deals with the child, its development, care and diseases.

potassium. A silver-white soft, light metallic element of the alkali metal (soluble salt) group that occurs abundantly in nature in combined forms.

saline. Consisting of or containing salt.

sodium citrate. A crystalline salt used in medicine as an anti-blood clotting agent.

toxic. Something poisonous.

Sources

BOOKS

Fleming, G. James, and Burckel, Christian E., eds., *Who's Who in Colored America,* Seventh edition. New York, Christian E. Burckel & Associates, 1950.

Lamb, Albert R., M.D., *The Presbyterian Hospital and the Columbia Presbyterian Medical Center 1868–1943: A History of a Great Medical Adventure.* New York, Columbia University Press, 1955.

Rothe, Anna, ed., *Current Biography.* New York, H. H. Wilson Company, 1950.

Sterne, Emma Gelders, *Blood Brothers: Four Men of Science.* New York, Alfred A. Knopf, 1959.

PERIODICALS AND REPORTS

"American Red Cross Blood Donor Service During World War II." (report) American Red Cross, Washington, D.C., July, 1946.

"America's Best Negro High School." *Ebony,* June, 1954.

Cobb, W. Montague, M.D., "Charles Richard Drew, M.D., 1904–1950." *Journal of the National Medical Association,* Vol. 42, no. 4, July, 1950.

Deutsch, Albert, "Dr. Charles Drew, Surgeon—A Study in Blood and Race." *PM Daily* (New York), March 30, 1944.

Hepburn, David, "The Life of Dr. Charles R. Drew." *Our World Magazine,* July, 1950.

Jones, Frank R., M.D., "Surgical Residents Training Program at Freedmen's Hospital." *Journal of the National Medical Association,* Vol. 52, no. 3, May, 1960.

McLaughry, D. O., "The Best Player I Ever Coached." *The Saturday Evening Post,* December 6, 1952.

"Prologue to Blood Plasma." *What's New Magazine* (Abbott Laboratories), December, 1944.

"Report of the Blood Transfusion Association Concerning the Supplying of Blood Plasma to England." Blood Transfusion Association, New York, January, 1941.

Scudder, John, M.D., "Practical Genetic Concepts." *Journal of the National Medical Association,* Vol. 52, no. 4, July, 1960.

Index

Adams, Dr. Numa P. G., dean of Howard University Medical School, 73, 76, 77, 78, 79, 99, 100, 102, 133–134
American Red Cross, 127, 129, 137
  blood for the, 131–132
Amherst College, 33, 34, 37, 47

Banked Blood, Drew's doctoral thesis, 109–110, 115
Beattie, John, 65–67, 68, 69–70, 71, 72, 91, 93, 118–121, 122, 130
Bethune, Dr. Norman, 71, 93
blood
  experiments with, 71
  non-Caucasian, not acceptable to Armed Forces, 131–132, 133
  preservation and storage of, 70, 81, 82, 83, 85
blood bank, 81, 82, 84, 85, 93, 95, 105–107, 110, 115, 120, 137
blood groups. *See* Landsteiner
blood research, 79, 81, 82–86, 89–91, 93–96
Blood Transfusion Association, 108, 111–115, 116, 117–132
blood transfusions, 69–70, 71, 100, 101, 102
Burrel, Grandpa Joe, 13–15, 19
Bush, John, president of the Blood Transfusion Association, 113, 122, 124, 125

Carrel, Dr. Alexis, 112, 113
Clark, Daniel "Pinky," Morgan College athlete, 50–51, 52, 53, 54, 57
Cobb, Montague, 33, 34, 35, 41, 43, 72, 78
Columbia-Presbyterian Medical Center, N.Y., 77, 79, 104

Drew, Charles Richard
  academic record of, at McGill, 67, 68
  as an athlete, 16–18, 22, 23, 26, 27, 29, 32, 34–35, 45
  birth of, 11–12
  characterization of, 31, 32, 45
  childhood of, 13–23
  children of, 123, 129, 135
  death of, 139
  degrees won by, 47, 68, 104, 115
  internship at Montreal General Hospital, 68
  marriage of, 107
  as a student, 22, 23, 25, 26, 29, 37, 44
  trophies won by, 46
Drew, Elsa, 12, 13, 29
Drew, Eva, 13, 47, 62
Drew, Joe, 12, 13, 14, 15, 22, 23
Drew, Lenore, 123, 129
  See also Robbins, Lenore.
Drew, Nora (mother of Charles), 12, 14, 24, 26–27, 28, 47
Drew, Nora (sister of Charles), 12
Drew, Richard, 12, 14, 15, 24, 27, 28, 47, 62, 68–69, 75

Fantus, Dr. Bernard, 81, 82, 93
Foggy Bottom, Washington, D.C., 11, 13, 18–19, 22, 47
Freedmen's Hospital, 75–76, 78, 80, 81, 116, 134–135, 136, 137

Gilmer, George, 34, 35, 41, 43
Glaser, Dr. Otto, professor of biology at Amherst, 37–38

Harvey, William, 66, 87–89
Hastie, William, 25, 33, 41, 43, 46

Index

Howard University Medical School
- assistant professorship for Drew at, 116, 119, 121
- Drew's application to, rejected, 56–57, 58, 60
- instructorship in pathology at, for Drew, 73, 75

Howes, Dr. Edward L., Professor of Surgery at Howard University, 76–80, 83, 99, 134

Jason, Dr. Robert, 138–139
Jorda, Duran, 81, 92, 112

Landsteiner, Karl, Nobel prizewinner, 65–66, 69, 71, 91, 96–98, 100, 112, 114

Malpighi, Marcello, 88–89
McGill University, Montreal, Canada, 58
- application to, by Drew, 59–60
- Drew's graduation from, 68
- Drew's years at, 62–66
- record made by Drew at, 73

McLaughry, D. O. "Tuss," 34, 37, 40, 43–44, 45, 48–49, 64–65
Montreal General Hospital
- Drew's internship at, 68, 69–72
- Drew's residency in surgery at, 72, 73

Morgan College, 48–60

Paul Laurence Dunbar High School, 25, 28, 30, 32
plasma, 95–96, 108, 109, 111, 113–114, 118, 121, 138
- for Britain, 122–128, 129, 137
- for France, 114, 116
- for the Red Cross, 129

Rh factor, 97–98
Robbins, Lenore, 101, 102–103, 107. *See also* Drew, Lenore.
Rockefeller Foundation, 76, 77, 79

Scudder, Dr. John, 77, 79, 80, 81–83, 84–86, 91–92, 95, 96, 100, 103–105, 108, 110, 111, 113, 115, 124, 125, 127, 128
Spencer, Dr. John, president of Morgan College, 48–49, 55–56
Stoddard, Helen, head nurse of Columbia-Presbyterian blood bank, 105–106

Whipple, Dr. Allen O., professor of surgery at Columbia University's Medical School, 77, 78, 84, 102, 104–105
Wilson, Edward, registrar at Morgan College, 55–56, 57–58, 60